MW00650799

Reconnective Therapy

A New Healing Paradigm

by
Herwig Schoen

RCT Publishing
Langley, Washington

Reconnective Therapy: A New Healing Paradigm
Second Edition
by Herwig Schoen

Cover design: Phil Dexter
Cover illustration based on a painting by Herwig Schoen
Cover illustration graphic work: Eric Falk
Illustrations: Alice Griffin
Editor: Cynthia Lane

Second Edition 2012
Printed in the United States of America

Library of Congress Catalog Card Number: 2011914094
ISBN: 978-0-615-52330-9

Published by:
RCT Publishing
5326 Mina Lane
Langley, WA 98260
USA
orders@reconnectivetherapy.com
www.reconnectivetherapy.com

This book is dedicated to all those who are on their way home.

Table of Contents

Preface

My intent in writing this book is to share the many insights that I have received since I began practicing Reconnective Therapy. I think that sharing and networking are among the most important things that we can contribute to the survival of humanity on planet Earth. This book and the teachings on Reconnective Therapy are part of my contribution.

Everything that I write about is drawn from my own experience. As long as we have "perception"—meaning that we see ourselves as separate from what we perceive—we will have as many truths as we have people. Once we remember our oneness with everything, perception will cease to exist and we will have knowing. This knowing is truth that is beyond what words can communicate.

Disclaimer

Reconnective Therapy is not a medical treatment. All that we do is shift frequencies. When we use the term “diagnosis” in connection with Reconnective Therapy, it means that we know what the body is asking us to treat. The term “treatment” refers to facilitation of the connections between the energy body and the physical body in the ways described below.

Acknowledgments

First, I want to acknowledge the ground breaking work of osteopathy's founders, Dr. Still and Dr. Sutherland. While I have not read their works, numerous talks with a good friend, who is an osteopathic physician, introduced me to the tremendous knowledge and insight of these men. I came to understand that the original osteopathy is high-level energy work that uses principles similar to those of Reconnective Therapy. Drs. Still and Sutherland explored the terrain until they reached the breath of life, which, if I understand it correctly, is a rhythm that connects all life. Few contemporary osteopaths seem to know about this or incorporate it into their work. However, as I see it, Drs. Still and Sutherland laid the ground on which we as practitioners of RCT stand today.

The teachings that I received in manual therapy from the Upledger Institute in Germany and DCR (Dialogs in Contemporary Rehabilitation) gave me the basic understanding of how the body really works.

I also want to acknowledge the discipline of lightbody surgery. The extraordinary skill and knowledge of three of its representatives helped me raise my frequency to a level that made it possible for me to enter into the work that I do today. Their insights gave me a framework for understanding how RCT fits into the bigger picture.

Finally, I want to express my gratitude and love for all those on my path who were and still are teachers, supporters and friends, whether they live on this side of physical reality or not. Without all of you, what I call Reconnective Therapy would probably not have happened in the way that it did and still does. Thanks to all of you.

Warning

Please do not ever attempt to use the information about the frequencies for treatments, especially not through visualization, as long as you are not connected to them in the way that I describe in Chapter 5. You can potentially damage yourself and others.

1

Introduction

Reconnective Therapy (RCT) is a new concept that presents a different and, in some ways, expanded way to look at things. For this reason, I recommend that you read this book chapter by chapter. This will help to avoid misunderstandings.

Talking about RCT can be tricky, because we are accustomed to using words to describe things on the three-dimensional plane. RCT connects information from beyond three-dimensional reality into our bodies and minds and facilitates healing and evolution from there.

The laws of higher-frequency realms are quite different from third-dimensional laws. For example, space and time, as we know it here, do not exist in the higher realms. Therefore, things are found everywhere, rather than in particular locations. Past and future also do not exist. Everything takes place in the present moment. If you contemplate this a bit, you might get a feeling for it and see that words cannot accurately convey this kind of reality.

These higher-frequency realms are your home. You all know them, have memories of them and are able to connect with them to certain degrees, consciously or unconsciously. As I start talking about this, the words and experiences they transmit might serve as a bridge for you to connect to what you have forgotten since you came here.

In my understanding, the mind rules everything. The mind has an infinite power of which most of you are probably not even remotely aware. Your beliefs and feelings create your experiences. It is not my intention to have you automatically accept the information that I share as true, and start to create your reality according to its premises. Rather, I want the information that I offer to serve as a door opener into higher aspects of yourself. This might only work if you always stick to what you feel is real in yourself.

In this book, I describe *my* experiences and *my* interpretations of them. Yours might be different. This does not imply that one is right and one is wrong, but rather that you hold a different and absolutely unique aspect of unity that you came to express here in polarity. One of the purposes of the treatments and the teachings that I offer—and this book—is to help you find this in yourself.

Before this book can delve into how RCT works and what it can do, I need to define some terms and concepts that are fundamental to its understanding. In Chapter 2, I show why a force that organizes matter into a physical body must exist. I call this force the "energy body." From there, I go into the realms of energy and dimensions, and their interconnection with our perception and what we call reality. Then I present a bigger picture of what the human experience is about—the next piece of the puzzle in comprehending RCT.

Chapter 5 provides a little map that can guide you through the process of the transformation of the energy body and the structures into which humankind is evolving. It describes the frequencies with which RCT works, including what they look like, what kind of information they hold and what they can do.

By the end of Chapter 5, all the pieces are together. In Chapter 6, I can therefore delineate how RCT works. Chapter 7 takes this a step further and goes into how the mind connects to and interacts with the physical body, how it protects itself—and can be healed.

Chapter 8 is a short excursion into the laws of healing and the allopathic and homeopathic principles. I designed it to provide a structure for healing work in general and for relating RCT to these principles. In Chapter 9, you learn that RCT works beyond causality, the meaning of this and its relation to what the Bible calls "grace."

Before you read Chapter 12, it is important that you understand two things: (i) From the viewpoint of RCT, dysfunction does not exist; and (ii) what RCT can accomplish.

Chapter 12 is the largest part of this book. More than thirteen years of practicing RCT, along with some of the teachings I received, have given me a much broader insight into the structure and function of the physical body than either my medical education or the current medical school curricula provide. In this chapter, I share both my knowledge and experiences, mostly by using the categories and terms of Western medicine. In so doing, I present a broader understanding of various conditions, ranging from bad moods to broken necks. I tried to limit this chapter to knowledge not commonly held by healthcare practitioners, but which might be important to facilitate healing.

2

The Energy Body

In this chapter, I will show that physical matter does not structure itself into organized forms by itself. Only a force can accomplish this.

The equations of theoretical physics provide one way to describe physical reality. Newton's laws, for example, are expressed in equations that accurately describe physical reality in the dimensions that are directly accessible to our senses. These equations form the foundation for many aspects of theoretical and applied science. They are used, for instance, in the structural engineering of every building.

Two axioms compose the foundation of classical, Newtonian mechanics. One is $F = m \cdot a$, which means that force equals mass times acceleration. Nothing has ever invalidated this axiom, not even the evolution of quantum theory.

$F = m \cdot a$, tells us that no piece of matter ever budges unless a force moves it. I can say it this way because the ideal situation of friction-free movement does not exist in the physical world.

I want to apply this insight to the formation of a human cell. Many different elements go into making a cell. We find oxygen, hydrogen, carbon, nitrogen and a lot of minerals. However, if we take all the cell's components and put them together in a bowl in exactly the right proportions, we will not create a living cell. We can try whatever we want—stir, shake, heat or whatever— we still will not have a cell, just a group of elements mixed together in a bowl.

What, then, distinguishes the mixture of elements from a living cell? A force must organize the components in a way that manifests a cell. Once this force acts upon these elements, we see them bonding to each other and moving around in a way that is clearly a living cell. When this force disconnects from the cell, we see all the elements start to separate from each other again and go their own ways. We see the cell falling apart, or, we say the cell has died.

With this, we can perceive a cell as a dynamic event in which an intelligent force organizes matter in a specific way, rather than as a gathering of matter that over time and by coincidence evolves a form of organization in order to survive. Evolution, in my understanding, is the manifestation of these organizing forces in space and time.

If we fully accept this concept—that a force organizes matter—

the way we see the world changes drastically. We perceive everything in the physical world as the expression of an organizing, living force. This force can be seen as the counterbalance to the second law of thermodynamics, which says that everything in the created universe tends towards entropy.

Now, I want to apply these insights to the human body. What is valid for one cell should be valid for a unit consisting of many cells. Just as a force organizes matter in the creation of one cell, it also organizes the manifestation of a physical body. This force is the energy body to which I referred in the Introduction.

The energy body has a distinct anatomy. It holds all the information for body shape, structure and function. It holds all our feelings, thoughts and memories. Everything that we have experienced or will experience is in our energy bodies. It holds all our possible futures as well as all our higher aspects that have not yet connected to the body. It holds all the possibilities for raising our frequency up to the level of our pure essence. We can say that the physical body is a materialized expression of parts of our energy body. I say parts, because our energy body is vast. For most of us, our physical bodies are connected to just a tiny bit of its information.

The electromagnetic system—the information pathways of electromagnetic current within the body, as well as its electromagnetic field—is sometimes mistaken for the energy body. However, this system, generated by the interaction of energy and physical matter, is just a small aspect of the energy body.

All of us have the senses to perceive and read the energy body.

Once we have acquired some skill in this, we can diagnose the physical body with great precision and reliability, because, as previously stated, the energy body contains all the information about the physical body. Many of us have heard of people who do this. Our culture calls them clairvoyants or medical intuitives. Caroline Myss is a well-known example.

3

About Energy: *The Dimensional Model*

It is important to realize that we cannot access force directly, because it does not originate in the three-dimensional realm. I don't think that anybody knows what force actually is; we can only see how it manifests. We also cannot measure force. We can only perceive and measure its impact.

Physics measures the impact of force on physical matter, but the impact is not the force. It is a manifestation of force in the three-dimensional realm. For example, force can manifest as electric current, which is force moving electrons through a conductor. The movement of the electrons is not the force itself, but a way that force can manifest in the three-dimensional plane. Physical manifestation follows certain laws, and discovering these laws and regularities is the business of physics.

In order to understand Reconnective Therapy, we need to look into things from a larger perspective than that of the physical world. This means that we have to use more than our five senses, which are designed to orient us in the physical universe. To orient ourselves in the energetic world, we have to use energetic perception. To understand things beyond the physical realm, we have to use the parts of our mind that can go beyond causality.

For example, we know today that our eyes see only a small spectrum of electromagnetic waves, compared to the frequencies that science has observed. If we want our perception to go beyond this limited spectrum, we have to use different senses. For example, we cannot see the infrared spectrum with our eyes, but we can feel it on our skin as warmth.

In this chapter, I want to describe physical reality as a certain spectrum within a far bigger continuum of frequencies. For this, I will use the model of dimensions. The first dimension is the straight line, or what we call length. The second dimension is the plane, which has both length and width. The third dimension, or what we call space, extends in three directions: length, width and height.

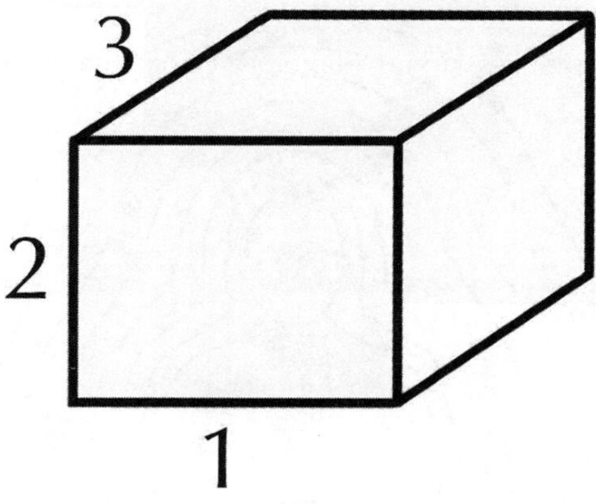

Picture 3.1.

These three dimensions make up our physical world. Our five senses—vision, hearing, smell, taste and touch—are configured to help us function within this structure. If we go to higher dimensions that do not contain any physical matter, these senses do not perceive anything that is present.

If we go past the three-dimensional world, we can view reality as layers of frequencies similar to the organization of an onion. These layers are bundled in a certain order. Therefore, after the three-dimensional world, we have the fourth dimension, which has seven harmonics.

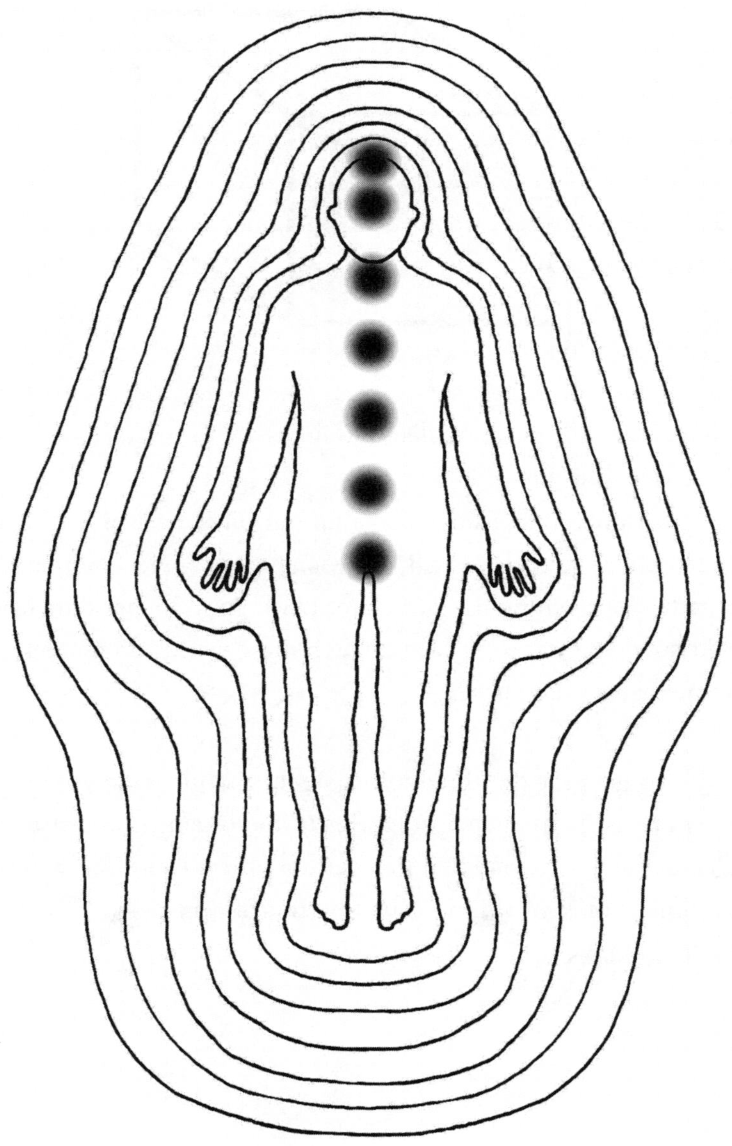

Picture 3.2.

As we can see, these seven harmonics relate to seven layers in the energy body and seven energy centers or *chakras*, as they are called in Sanskrit, the ancient language of India. The first harmonic relates to the base chakra, the second to the navel chakra and so on. Every layer seems to vibrate at a distinct frequency. Similarly, in the model of the atom that goes back to Niels Bohr, electrons exist on distinct energy levels or frequencies that surround the nucleus. This parallel does not surprise me, since I understand that everything follows the same basic universal templates. Some people have told me that the distances between the sun and the planets have the same ratios as those between an atomic nucleus (composed of protons and neutrons) and the electrons that orbit it.

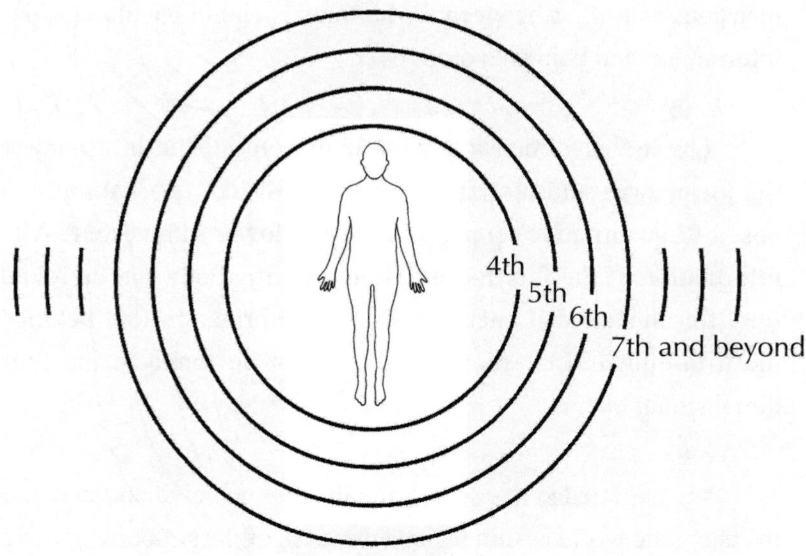

Picture 3.3.

The fifth dimension comes next, with twelve harmonics. I have often seen that the movement of energy in this dimension looks much like the Hebrew alphabet. Then we have the sixth dimension with its twenty-four harmonics, and so it continues, probably indefinitely.

Between every two dimensions, beginning with the fourth, I have observed transitional frequencies that stand by themselves and do not belong directly to the structure of any dimension. They function as transitions between the dimensions Generally the dimensions as well as their harmonics are sealed against each other in a certain way. You have to have a certain level of vibratory frequency to be able to cross from one harmonic into another or from one dimension into another. This is a very important function as certain information or beings have to be contained in certain areas otherwise they can cause a lot of damage. There is a possibility to open portals between the dimensions as well as between the harmonics within one dimension for information and beings to cross over.

The higher dimensions appear to hold all the information of the lower ones and more. They are almost like qualitative (as opposed to quantitative) expansions of the lower dimensions. All the information of the fourth-dimensional energy body can be found in the fifth-dimensional energy body, but information that belongs to the fifth-dimensional energy body cannot be found in the fourth-dimensional one.

My experience has shown me that we perceive and understand the energetic world as dimensional because of the structure of our perception, and not because it is the way things are. Though it is not easy to communicate these experiences, I will try and explain this a little more, with the hope that you will get a feeling for what I describe.

Perception needs more than our senses; it requires participation by the mind. If we look at a wonderful green tree just with our senses and without the mind's involvement, we only get an impression of green. In fact, we do not even get this, because green is already an interpretation by the mind. All we can experience is a certain sensation or feeling without any idea about what it might be. The tree becomes a tree for us because we have agreed to interpret and see a certain impression as that. From a deeper level, we can say that the tree, as a part of creation, is in us, and we connect to it by looking at it on the physical level. This is like creation looking at itself through human eyes.

Space and time provide another useful example. They have no independent reality; they are structures of our perception. The perception of space and time is one of the things that make up our collective experience of polarity and, on the physical plane, we perceive each energy that presses on our senses through the structure of space and time.

Let's go back to our dimensional model. At this point in our evolution, our minds work largely by splitting things apart. We see things as separate from each other, as we do with the dimensions: body and mind, thinking and feeling, plus and minus, and so on. If we go beyond our perceptual structures, dimensions do not exist. Everything is one; everything is a unit.

4

The Human Experience: *A Bigger Picture*

When we start to talk about the human experience, we begin to move into a bigger picture, because it implies that a non-human experience is also possible. We can approach this in many ways, but I chose the one with which I resonate the most.

Let's say that at one time, we all lived in unity. I don't yet know how to describe unity in words, but I think we all get glimpses of it once in a while. I feel as if it lives inside me as a memory of home, a hope, a sense of something that I both know and am looking for all the time in everything and everyone. It is like a joy ready to burst forth, or a child's sense of expectation under the Christmas tree just as the presents are about to be handed out. At the same time, this memory has the feeling of something much more vast than all this.

When we live in unity, nothing that we feel or see is separate from ourselves. This is our natural state of being, the truth of who we are.

At some point, however, the idea that we are different, different from our brothers and sisters, arises. When this idea enters our minds, we see ourselves as being separate or different, though this does not mean that we actually are different. As I see it, this kind of thoughts lower our frequency and we split. The split occurs between the person we really are and the person we think we are. In other words, we continue being the person living in oneness, while the part that splits thinks that it is singular, unconnected. The reality of unity stays untouched, while the divisive thought spins another reality where we experience the illusion of being different.

My use of the term illusion in this context refers to the mind's creative power to turn thought into something real for us. Bear in mind that this does not mean that the mind's creation *is* real. An unreal thought or condition, or an illusion, has to be fed constantly. It has to be re-created over and over and all the time, or it will collapse. To experience what is real, we just have to relax and do nothing because it is always there. It is indestructible, and it will take over when we allow it to do so.

Every thought that is not in alignment with spirit or our true nature lowers our frequency and leads to another split. Every possibility within every split is held in a so-called parallel reality, like a gigantic library. What we experience right now is the book that we have chosen to read.

Let me give an example on a small scale to clarify this. Let's say you get into a fight with your spouse and you have to choose between a loving response and anger and fighting back. If you decide to fight back, you split. Your frequency lowers and you experience the opportunity for the aggressive reaction. At the same time, a separate reality that you have decided not to experience holds the loving response. Later on, by yourself, you think about what happened. You now see the option of a loving, understanding response, and you resolve to go back to your loved one to communicate your insights and try to heal the wounds. You will find that the wounds will heal, regardless of how your partner reacts. Your frequency will rise and the former split will heal. If anger gets the upper hand again and you react accordingly, you will experience another split, and another parallel reality will hold the loving response that you chose not to adopt.

At this point, I want to make it clear that no judgment is involved in this. I do not say that one decision is better than the other. We have the freedom to experience whatever we choose.

The more often we split, the more we think we are separate, and the more we lose the memory of who we truly are. This can go so far that we no longer know anything about our real selves. Even if we experience just a tiny piece of our real self, it might appear so alien that our mind sees it as something unreal and forgets about it. This is the place where most of us are right now.

Some of us might fear being lost forever. I do not think that this is possible. We did not create ourselves thus we will not be able to destroy ourselves.

The process of splitting and lowering our frequencies can continue for a long time. We not only split in the reality of which we are consciously aware, but also in the parallel realities of which we are unaware. Every split spins another parallel reality, and so they build. We can see that over a period of many tens of thousands, or even hundreds of thousands of years, the number of splits that occur and the number of parallel realities we spin can be awesome.

At some point, usually in the deepest of all darknesses, we decide that enough is enough. We see that the way we have been living hasn't given us anything we really want. Often, we no longer have the foggiest idea of who we are and what can help, and we start to question. We begin to give up our old ways of thought and action, because we see that they don't get us anywhere. We are now willing to open ourselves for something helpful to happen, whatever it might be.

Once we choose to heal and go back to unity, one lifetime typically reflects the process I just described, i.e., falling out of unity and opening up for healing. As infants, we are very much in unity, but then we forget and start going our own ways. We usually get a wakeup call eventually, often in the form of an illness or accident. As a result, we give up the path we have been following and ask for help. We open ourselves up for things to happen that are far beyond the understanding of our conscious minds. With this decision, we embark upon the journey of healing, which is the most beautiful and exciting adventure I know.

The good news in all this is that our true nature has never been touched. The moment we give up and allow it to come forth, it will. It is as natural and inevitable as water flowing downhill. This is where RCT comes onto the scene. As I will describe later in detail, RCT is a tool to connect higher aspects of ourselves into our bodies in a very specific way that helps us to reconnect to who we really are. This will happen at some point anyway, but RCT is a way to speed up this process tremendously.

With the healing process—or, in other words, with the raising of our frequency—all the parallel realities that we have created along the way merge back together. This is a gigantic procedure and most of us are completely unconscious of it most of the time. The splits that we have undergone since we fell out of unity heal and we increasingly become one piece. This is the meaning of becoming more integrated.

In this context, I want to say something about the memory of past lives. I won't go into all the pros and cons about whether past lives are real or not, but simply state that they are one way to interpret certain experiences. If you go into an esoteric bookstore and buy and read a book about human history from someone who remember parts of his past, you will find an impressive amount of information that largely makes sense, as long as you read only that book. If you read other books, most of them will seem to contradict each other. I believe that this occurs because people tap into the memories of parallel realities.

When I started having memories of past lives, everything seemed authentic. Then I had so many memories of the last 400 years, for example, that they could not fit into that time frame. I did not know what to do with this until I understood the bigger picture of parallel realities. Richard Bach has written a wonderful book on this topic, called *One*.

At this point, we usually start to ask, "Why?" Why did we do this sometimes-so-outrageously painful thing? Why didn't we just stay in unity?

I cannot answer this question with any finality; I can only share my personal vision, based on my own experience. Sometimes I can see myself and everything around me as an expansion of God. Unity is one experience. If we take on separation, God can see Himself[1] through our eyes in a completely new way. He can look at Himself from a distance that has not been possible before. Everything we experience on this planet as human beings is an experience that God is having. I feel that bringing Him all these experiences is my gift to Him, and the more fully I engage in life's possibilities, the more I have to give.

A good friend of mine added another viewpoint. He said that as long as we are in unity, we don't have a choice whether to be there or not. Only from polarity can we consciously decide whether to be in unity or not. This adds a whole other quality to the experience of unity.

As I look at what is happening on planet Earth, it appears to me that we are in a time of tremendous opportunities for healing and integration. I see RCT as one of the tools given to facilitate this process.

---

1 I'm aware that God transcends gender. I choose the term "Him" because I have to operate within the limitations of the English language.

5

The Transformation of the Energy Body

On our way back to unity, most of us start with a fourth-dimensional energy body with seven chakras that correlate with the energy body's seven layers. As we heal, our frequency rises. Once the frequency goes beyond a certain threshold, the structure and function of the energy body undergo profound change, a shift that has already begun for many people. In this chapter, I am going to describe the process of change in as much detail as I can, though I want to make it clear that I do not yet have the complete picture. I am learning about it constantly, and I may have more information even as this book goes into print. Nevertheless, experience has shown that this does not invalidate the information that I am sharing; it just extends it.

Chapter Five

For the purposes of this book, I define frequency in quantum mechanical terms, using the equation, $E = h \cdot n$, which basically means that the higher the frequency, the greater the energy. Each frequency holds a certain quality and information. I also use the dimensional map that I laid out in Chapter 3, as well as another map for what I call the centers. Please keep in mind that these structures are ways of perception and not reality itself. They offer a way for the mind that is still operating within polarity to relate to information about energy.

Many books competently describe the human energy system at the frequency level that I portrayed in Chapter 3 as the fourth-dimensional energy body. It consists of seven frequencies which correlate with seven chakras or energy centers and seven layers in the energy body. The shape of the chakras is a double vortex with vortices inscribed. The uppermost and lowest ones are only single vortices. The five lower chakras originate in particular places in the spinal cord. The uppermost two originate in the pituitary and pineal glands. Each chakra has a color associated with it, starting with violet in the crown and going down through the frequencies to red in the base chakra. Each layer of the energy body contains specific information about body and mind structure and function. If we use music as an analogy, we can think of these seven frequencies as one octave.

Once the body starts connecting to higher-frequency information, the structure of the energy body changes in a specific way. When I try to understand these changes in a bigger context, it looks to me as if the energy body is losing structure.

As Chapter 4 explained, our natural state of being is oneness. Words cannot do it justice. In the state of oneness, we remember who we are and that the belief in separateness from God or anything in the universe has no reality. It is intriguing to contemplate how much complex structure unity can contain, since structure divides things and defines their differences. When we get close to the basis of creation, we end up with only a few principles from which all creation derives.

I have observed that the changes in the energy body seem to follow a certain pattern. At first, the colors in the field progressively disappear and white replaces them. Interestingly, white light contains every color. Consequently, when a prism breaks white light into its components, all the colors emerge. By raising the frequency, a complex structure becomes simpler, yet retains all its information. Its complexity is revealed if its motion slows, by running it through a prism, for example. Later, we'll see that this perfectly mirrors the process of lowering the frequency that has been part of the journey for many people.

The chakras turn from double or single vortices into spheres. The vortices shrink back into the body as the spheres emerge. This transformation usually starts in the upper chakras in the head and then travels down into the body until it reaches the base chakra. In the next step, the chakras unify, so that places of higher and lower energy no longer exist. Instead, the energy body becomes a unified field.

In the fourth-dimensional energy body, energy comes into the body through the crown chakra and is transformed downwards in frequency through the other chakras. With the connection to higher frequencies, energy stops entering through the crown chakra and instead comes out of the cells. This happens through the DNA, which serves as an antenna or gateway into the dimensions from which the energy infusing into the body comes. These changes appear to be part of our evolution and I see them happening in increasing numbers of people.

I have encountered another way to look at the energy body besides the structure of dimensions which I just discussed. In this case, the energy body looks like it has several major centers that hold different qualities of information. These centers are not located in the body like chakras, nor do they resemble chakras in any way. As I experience them, they hold information that is so vast that I have not yet found words for it. However, I can describe aspects of the seven frequencies of the first center, the first two frequencies of the second and the general quality of the second and third centers. I am familiar with a few more frequencies of the second, third, fourth and fifth centers, but again, I don't yet have the words or understanding to portray them adequately. When I mention a frequency without attributing it to a specific center, that frequency always belongs to the first center.

In every dimension, regardless of how high it may be, there is a possibility for distortion, which means it can contain information about dysfunction. The centers do not have that. They do not contain any information about dysfunction whatsoever. They seem to be a translation that allows perfection to connect into structures created by the belief in separation.

The information contained in the frequencies of these centers connects to the body through certain interfaces. An interface is something like a translation device to connect structures that speak different languages. For example, take a human being and a computer. If someone talks to his computer and tells it what to do, the computer does not respond, because it cannot understand the instructions. It speaks a different language. The interface between the individual and his computer is the keyboard. The keyboard speaks both languages. It has letters on its keys and when the individual presses them, the keyboard translates them into digital impulses that the computer comprehends. The computer then communicates to the individual via the screen, which is another interface translating computer language into human language.

Energy interfaces appear to connect information from the energy body into the physical body. The information in your energy field does not do anything for you until it connects to your physical body. There, the energy interfaces translate the information into action. For example, the template for the structure and function of your right knee does not do you any good until it is translated into motion. The energy body holds the information and the interface translates it into a force that actively organizes physical matter into the structure and function of your knee the moment that this information is connected to the physical body.

In my experience, most people have access to the first frequency. If we want to use frequencies above that for treatments, our bodies have to be connected to at least the first two frequencies of the first center in a specific geometric pattern. This is like a little initiation. Only then will we be able to provide these frequencies in our bodies so that our clients can resonate with them and use them for healing. Addressing the interfaces for the higher frequencies without having this connection can lead to damage to others and ourselves. When the body and mind of the student are ready, a qualified RCT practitioner facilitates these initiations. Once practitioners are initiated into the first two frequencies, they spontaneously connect to higher frequencies when they are ready. Thus far, a spontaneous connection to second frequency and above seems to be a rare event. I have only seen it once.

I think that right now I know relatively little about the information held in these frequencies. It looks like the full impact of the information contained in the frequencies to which we connect in RCT is showing itself only to a small degree. The power of these connections will reveal more of themselves as humankind evolves into higher frequencies.

In RCT treatments, we can administer all the frequencies of the different centers distinctly, one by one, or all at once. To clarify this, remember that white light has every color, and that a prism can split white light into separate colors. Analogously, we can unify all the colors to produce white light, and apply them at the same time, or we can use different colors for treatments, one after another.

Generally, the higher frequencies contain the information of the lower ones.

It is important to understand that in a treatment, only tiny parts of the body are connected to the information held in the different frequencies. However, this has proven to be enough for even dramatic shifts in body structure, as well as the related patterns of thinking and feeling.

We now have two different ways to look at energy body structures, the centers and the dimensions. How can we bring them together? In other words, what information will be revealed if we look at one structure through the eyes of the other? I want to talk about one feature that is particularly interesting within the context of RCT.

As we have already discussed, higher-dimensional information contains all the lower- dimensional information, but not vice versa. If we want to connect, for example, sixth- dimensional information all the way into the physical body, we have to filter it through every harmonic of the fifth- and fourth-dimensional energy body into physicality. In most people, this could pose quite a challenge, because of the amount of trauma generally stored in these aspects of the energy body. We therefore need to clear a channel that could allow sixth-dimensional information to connect all the way down into the physical matter of the body. For the majority of clients, that might take quite a long time. However, first frequency has the information necessary to create a bypass. This means once we are able to connect first frequency, we can connect sixth- dimensional information straight into any aspect of the energy body, as well as the physical body, without having to go through all the harmonics in between. Second frequency can create seventh- dimensional bypasses and so on. We can also connect higher-frequency information to the body without having to pass through the lower frequencies. For example, a second-frequency connection does not have to pass through first frequency to connect to the body. This allows for an enormous acceleration of the healing process.

The Seven Frequencies of the First Center

At this juncture in my work, I see that almost every part of the body can serve as an energy interface to connect information of these frequencies into the physical body. That means that all parts of the body serve an energetic as well as physical purpose.

The First Frequency

The first frequency holds information about body and mind structure and function. It shows itself to me as the pattern that you see in Figure 5.1 on the next page. The straight lines in the drawing are grey double lines with small dots in the middle, as you can see in the enlarged part. The little dots are what the lightbody surgeons refer to as the "keepers." Let me explain what the keepers are.

The body is conscious of itself. It says to itself, "This is me." Every integral part of the body has this kind of self-awareness, whether it's an arm, an organ, a cell or an atom. They all work together to maintain the body's structure and function. The body also has systemic functions, such as digestion, that include many different body parts. These systemic functions are also conscious of themselves. I call them the keepers, in accord with the lightbody surgeons. Digestion, wound healing, detoxification, the subconscious mind, bones and teeth are all examples of systemic functions. Frank Lowen, of Desert Light Health Associates, refers to them as "the systems." He found a way to activate them through touching particular points on the physical body.

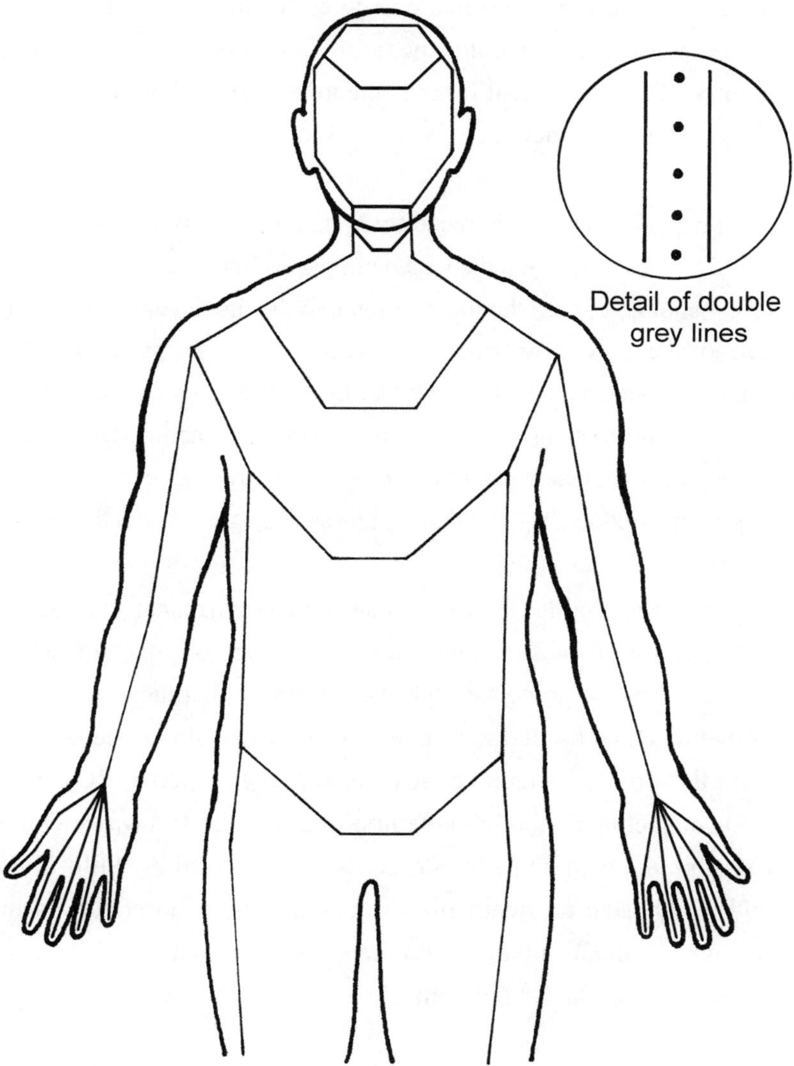

Fig. 5.1. First frequency double grey lines.

The first frequency contains information about body shape, structure and function, as well as the structure and function of the mind. In the fourth-dimensional energy body, the first layer, correlating with the base chakra, holds the information about how the body is structured. This means that it holds the information about function as well as current dysfunction.

Have you ever asked yourself why the body constantly rebuilds a tattoo? The reason is that the energetic impact of the tattooing procedure is strong enough to burn the information into the first layer of the fourth-dimensional energy body. Otherwise, a tattoo would fade as old skin cells die and new ones replace them. Unlike this part of the energy body, the first frequency contains absolutely no information about dysfunction. From what I have seen so far, I think that if the body was completely connected to this frequency, dysfunction, illness and aging would disappear.

Everybody has access to the first frequency. You can connect the first frequency of the first center directly to the body part on which you work, without going through the interfaces. It functions exactly the same way that I will describe in Chapter 6. You do not need initiation for this process, which you learn as the second step of RCT training. Reconnecting the body to the first frequency in this way includes working on the breath of life as described by Dr. Andrew Still. If you intentionally use it for treatments through the energy interfaces of the first center, without initiation into the second frequency, you can potentially damage clients and yourself.

Treatments with the first frequency that connect through the energy interfaces for the higher frequencies seem to have a far broader range of effects than those that connect the information directly through the body part you are treating. They appear to include a lot more related patterns in the emotional and mental system. For example, the body asks you to treat a lung with the first frequency. If you do the reconnection directly on the lung, you might mobilize the lung, and also help it to restructure some of its parenchyma. You might also help to heal some related emotional and mental patterns. However, if you go through the higher-frequency interfaces, you simultaneously address a lot more of the physical body structure, together with any related emotional and mental patterns. This means that healing through the interfaces goes a lot further than making the reconnection directly through the body part that you are treating.

Experience has shown that the body takes a longer time to integrate a treatment that goes through the higher-frequency interfaces than one that goes directly through the body part. The first usually takes around three-to-four weeks, if it is not an acute condition—the latter, about seven-to-ten days.

With few exceptions, we do all the treatments for the emotional body and the mental body, (see Chapter 7, page 95) as well as for the shock patterns, (see "Body Protection," page 156) with the first frequency.

The Second Frequency

As I see it, the second frequency holds information about the genetic code. Figure 5.2 shows how the second frequency looks to me. Let me try to explain the information it holds. Among other things, the genetic code is the material memory bank for the instructions for physical body structure and function. It tells every cell what to do and how to fulfill its role.

Every cell in the body has a specific job and DNA provides the information to carry it out. A liver cell knows how to participate in the work of the liver, and a skin cell knows how to play its role as skin. Every cell has a complete set of DNA with all the information for the whole body, but only the instructions relevant to the cell's specific function is active; the rest is blocked. For example, the DNA in a skin cell has complete information for every structure and function in the body, but the skin cell can only access the part of the DNA that tells it how to function as skin. The liver cell has access only to the part of the DNA that dictates liver cell activity. It cannot access instructions for functioning as a skin cell. I call this phenomenon the "coding of the body." Let's have a closer look at what this means.

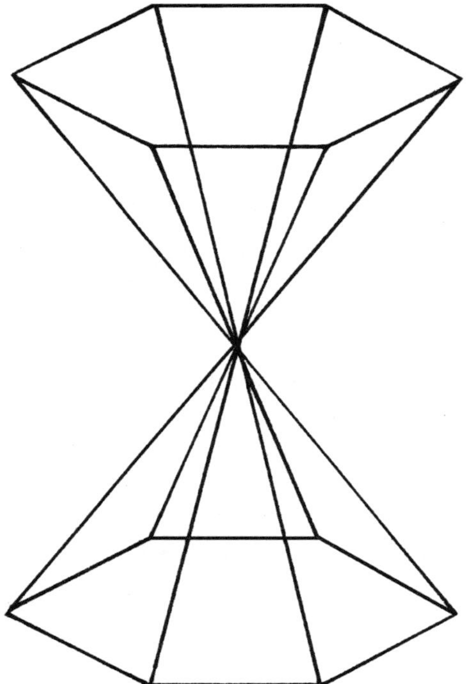

Fig. 5.2. Second Frequency.

The coding of the body keeps the different parts of the body separated from each other in their specific roles and allows only specific pathways of communication. Blood flow, for example, is separate from breathing. The only way that blood flow and breathing can communicate is through the alveoli of the lung, where an exchange of oxygen and carbon dioxide in the blood can take place. I see this coding as the physical manifestation of our idea of separateness. Unity means total communication; separation means limited communication.

The second frequency appears to hold the information on how to decode the body. I'll use an analogy to explain this further.

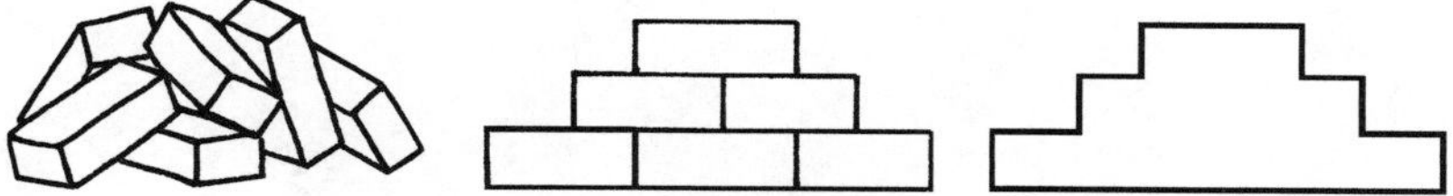

Fig. 5.3. Analogy explaining second frequency.

The first part of Figure 5.3 shows a stack of bricks randomly thrown together and completely unorganized. We now apply a force that holds the information for organizing the bricks into a wall and we see the result in the next picture. Finally, we connect a force to the bricks that holds the information of oneness and we have the third image.

The genetic code is matter organized into the beautiful, well-known form of the double helix. As we have already learned, a force must be present that holds the information of this structure and organizes matter in such a way that it manifests. We call this information a blueprint. The second frequency is not the blueprint of the DNA, but rather a vibrational pattern that creates this blueprint.

Figure 5.4 (below) shows how the second frequency is organized to create the blueprint for the coded body. Six of the symbols for the second frequency form a hexagon. The lines you see are the possible communication pathways between the larger hexagonal structures. Clearly, only limited communication exists among these larger structures, and only particular pathways and connections can be used.

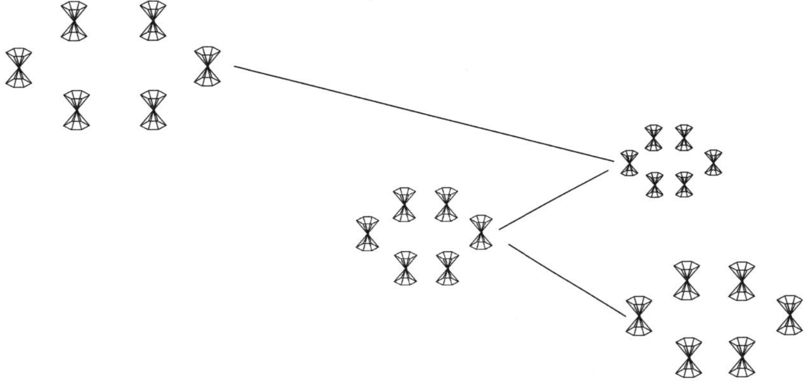

Fig. 5.4. Second frequency organized to create the blueprint for the coded body.

If the second frequency is connected to the body, the body's organization changes. The pattern is still organized in the shape of a hexagon, but we now find two of the second frequencies in every corner. (Figure 5.5) This structure is in total communication with all the other structures that are set up in the same way. I call this the "decoding of the body."

If second frequency is connected to the body in a RCT treatment, it usually connects to only minute areas of the body. The first thing that it seems to do is restructure DNA dysfunction. I have treated a number of genetically related diseases with good results.

The DNA appears to hold much more information than instructions for physical body structure and function. I can sense a quality that is almost like music, telling the body how to function differently on different frequency levels. In most people, the DNA appears to possess far greater information than is available at a given time. This is because it sleeps. Second frequency connection can wake up parts of the DNA that are asleep and make them accessible to the body. This process is intimately linked with internal growth and only the information that a person can handle will be connected.

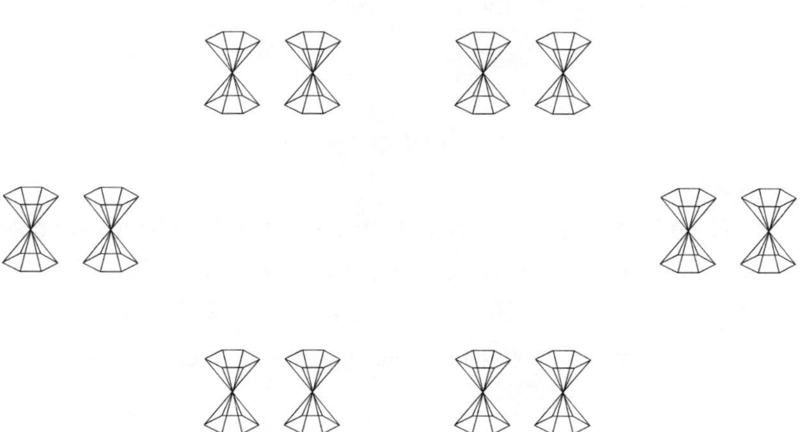

Fig. 5.5. Second frequency organized to create the decoded body.

I do not yet know how the decoding of the body actually shows up. However, if I extrapolate based on my existing information about the second frequency, I get a picture of what might happen once enough of the body connects to it. It looks as if the decoding of the body is preparing it to shift into a completely different way of being. In the body's current mode of functioning, the energy body organizes matter from planet Earth into the structure of the physical body. The second frequency seems to hold the information for setting the body up as a vibrational pattern that compresses energy in certain places on the three-dimensional plane and manifests a physical body in this way.

We can easily understand this phenomenon in physical terms. Einstein's equation, $E = mc^2$, means that energy equals matter times the speed of light to the second power. This tells us that physical matter is just highly compressed energy. When enough of second frequency is connected to the body, we will be able to manifest a physical body at will any place on the three-dimensional plane and live consciously in places higher than the three-dimensional world.

The Third Frequency

The third frequency is the only one about which I have ever read. I came across one small paragraph in a book called, *What is Lightbody?* which contains material channeled and recorded by Tachira Tachiren. This book describes the third frequency as the axiotonal lines.

I see third frequency as twenty-four red lines (Figure 5.6). They come out of the pituitary gland like water out of a fountain and then spread through the body. The lines somewhat resemble the meridian system, but a closer look at both reveals some significant divergence in their pathways. Five lines run through each extremity, each one ending in a toe or finger. Four lines run right next to the midline of the body, two in front and two in back. They meet approximately at the perineum.

Seeing these lines running through the body does not mean that they are connected to it. This information appears to connect into the body in particular places, through tiny energetic vortices. When this happens, it looks to me like little stars or dots of light.

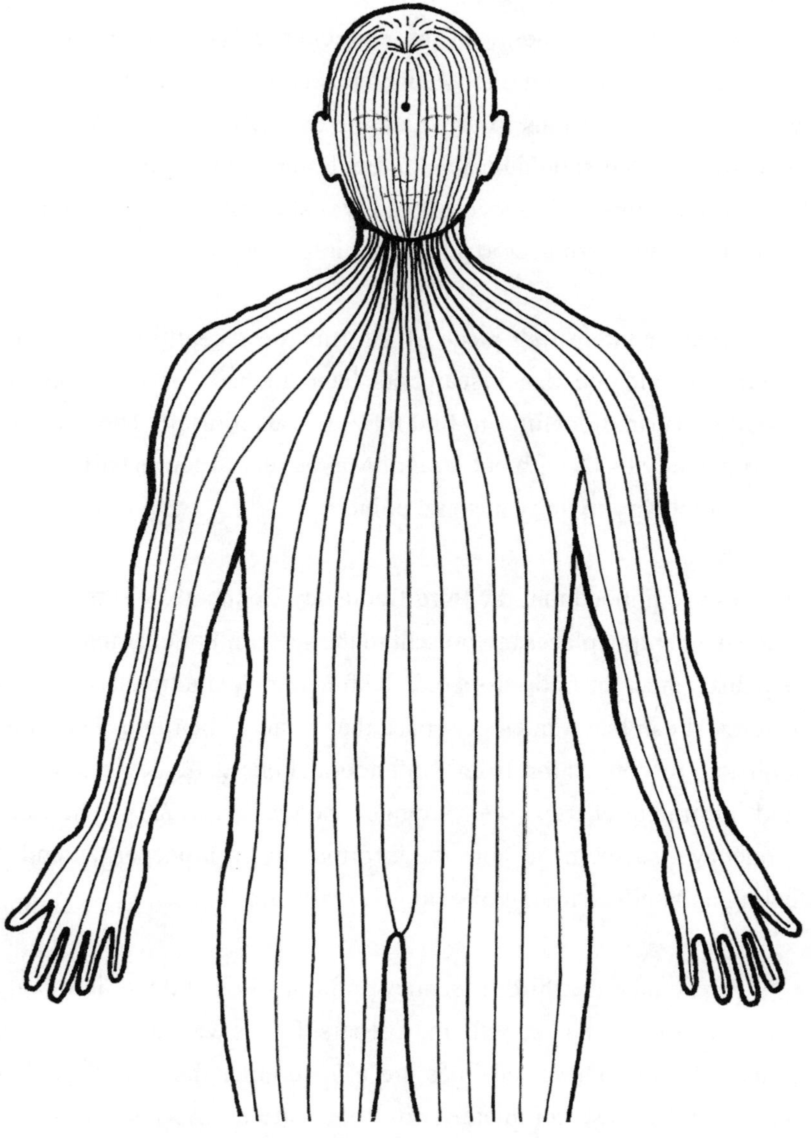

Fig. 5.6. The red lines of third frequency.

Though I only have a limited understanding of the third frequency, I do see that where it connects to the body, it transforms two-strand DNA into three-strand DNA. In the first part of this chapter, I explained that the energy in the new energy body comes into the physical body through the DNA, which serves as an antenna or gateway into the dimensions from which the energy connects. As I see it, three-strand DNA should be able to function as an antenna for a much broader spectrum of frequencies than two-strand DNA, which should allow the body to connect to a lot more information.

Another interesting piece of information recently came to me. Somebody told me that researchers have looked for DNA on the shroud of Turin, hopefully to find that of Jesus himself. The examiners found only DNA with one strand! Maybe this structure will also go from complexity to unity at some point.

I have noticed that the third frequency frequently wants to connect where empty places are present in the system. For example, if you help disconnect the body from old, dysfunctional, emotional or mental patterns, it can leave an empty space that wants to be filled. The same applies to disconnection from dysfunctional energetic devices or any kind of strange energy (see "Strange Energy," page 230). The third frequency also seems to hold the information for a deeper, extended feeling and understanding of who you really are.

If you take the third frequency and transform it down into body function, you will end up with the keepers. In this way, they also show up as red lines. These red lines are a lot thinner than the third frequency and follow completely different patterns. As I see it, every keeper has its own set of red lines that design fancy patterns in various parts of the body. This is not the third frequency, but rather the third frequency after it has been transformed down into body function.

Let me again use light to clarify this. As I explained earlier, if you run white light through a prism, you get a spread of colors. Each color, including red, is a split aspect of white and not white itself. In this way, the keepers are split aspects of the third frequency. The frequency you see when you look at the keepers is lower than the third frequency. The activation of the keepers does not connect the body to the third frequency. If you connect the body to the third frequency, you can usually see the activation of a number of keepers as well.

This has been a source of confusion for some practitioners who read or heard about the axiotonal lines. When they later saw the keepers' red lines, they mistook them for the third frequency.

The Fourth Frequency

To understand the fourth frequency, we have to look into how the body stores memory. I know of three ways so far: in the connective tissue, DNA structure and the inner structure of the body's physical matter. Let me briefly go through these three options.

1. Every sufficiently strong physical impact leaves an imprint in the connective tissue, which if untreated, can remain throughout life. Certain elements of connective tissue work like springs and shock absorbers in a car. However, unlike springs and shock absorbers, they do not revert to their original position if they are

exposed to too much physical force. Instead, they stay in a new position that shows the direction and magnitude of the impact as an imprint. In his books about craniosacral therapy, Dr. John Upledger describes the precise mechanics of this phenomenon.

2. It takes a significantly higher energy impact to leave an imprint in DNA than in connective tissue. This high energy accumulates due either to the body's exposure to the same information over a long period, perhaps years, or a very high energy within a short period.

As it looks to me, information has to have a strong emotional component to go into the genetic code. For example, if you receive a strong blow to your body in an accident, this information is stored in the structure of the connective tissue that received the blow, like an imprint. If this physical impact also carries an extreme emotional and mental threat, as in a rape, the information not only goes into the connective tissue, but also quite likely leaves its imprint in the DNA.

Most dogs have a soft, impressionable psyche. I have noticed that when dogs live with the same person over a number of years, they begin to look increasingly like that person, especially if the two of them have an intense relationship. I have observed the same thing in couples. After enough years of living together, the two of them start to look alike. Both these cases involve continuous exposure to the same information for a long time. As a result, enough energy builds up to register its imprint in the genetic code.

3. The French physicist Charon developed a theory that nicely explains and illustrates my experience with the body's third method of storing memory.

Fig. 5.7. Illustration of the inner time-space continuum.

Let the straight line in Figure 5.7 represent three-dimensional space and time, or the fourth-dimensional time-space continuum, as the physicists call it. If we bend this line until the ends cross over each other, we have one fourth-dimensional, time-space continuum inside the bubble that forms and one outside. According to Charon, when the time-space structure bends so that it forms this bubble, matter manifests. Therefore, he concludes that matter is not a solid structure, but a phenomenon that occurs when this bubble is created within the fourth-dimensional, time-space continuum. The outside of this bubble is time and space, as we all know it. The inside of the bubble is inaccessible to our five senses. The inside of the bubble serves as a memory bank for everything that ever happened to this particular piece of matter, all of which is stored there in specific vibrational patterns.

Some time ago, I heard about an experiment in which someone put a dying person onto a highly sensitive scale. At the moment of what we call death, the body lost a significant amount of weight. It is hard to tell exactly what happened. However, to put it as neutrally as I can, something that was creating weight left the body at that particular moment.

If we look at a person's history along the axis of linear time, we could interpret his experiences and memories in terms of multiple lifetimes on this planet. Each time an individual disconnects from one body—a phenomenon called death—he takes with him the same pieces of matter that serve as memory banks for every experience he has had since he connected to polarity and a physical body. This is what caused the weight loss in the dying person. When the individual connects to a woman's womb to grow a new body, these pieces of matter serve as seeds around which the new body builds. When new pieces of matter integrate with the body, some of them are imprinted with parts of the information that the seeds carry.

When the individual comes to planet Earth for another lifetime, he chooses certain tasks to learn and experiences to heal. Only the information he needs for this lifetime is activated in the seeds and contributes to the structure of his body and mind. The activated information also draws the experiences to him that he has chosen for this lifetime.

The inner structure of this matter does not store the events of former lifetimes, for they are neutral. However, it does store the way that a person relates to the events. This is an important distinction. The same event can have a totally dissimilar effect on different people, because they relate differently to it.

The fourth frequency has the capacity to open these memory banks and to connect a higher aspect of the persons self into them. With this, the way he relates to past life experience changes, along with the associated structures of his physical body. Most of the time this healing process completely bypasses the conscious mind of the people we treat. When the fourth frequency connects to the body, I have seen people integrate the experiences of whole causal chains, consisting of many lifetimes, in just one treatment. I will describe this whole process in a bigger context and a lot more detail in Chapter 7, page 95.

The Fifth Frequency:
The Activation of the Brainstem

When the fifth frequency started to show up in treatments, I was in a friend's home and a book by Paramahansa Yogananda fell into my hands. I opened it and read the following sentence: "The medulla (*medulla oblongata*) is the gate to heaven." This one sentence opened a new realm of understanding for me.

I have always viewed the connection of heaven and earth as a major purpose for living here. As I see it, living outside the physical body in the higher energy realms does not really do anything. When so-called "spirituality" does not connect to the physical body, it does not have much influence on the three-dimensional realm. On the other hand, living exclusively by identifying with physical form keeps us nicely grounded but does not bring any aspect of heaven into our body. Connecting the higher realms into the physical body and experiencing them in this way is one of the most amazing experiences I know. It can cause so much joy and excitement that they become contagious to all surrounding beings.

When I connect somebody to the fifth frequency, it always connects to the medulla first. From there, it moves down to the sacrum, which can take anywhere from a few moments to a few weeks. I see the sacrum as the part of our physiology that connects us to planet Earth.

Connecting the fifth frequency to the body connects the information of the lightbody blueprint—which might correlate with heaven or something close to it—to the brainstem, which Yogananda considered the gateway to heaven. From there, it moves down the spine until it hits the sacrum, the connection to Earth. There it is: the connection of heaven and earth within the physical body.

Because the fifth frequency always connects through the medulla into the body, I call it the brainstem activation. The brainstem activation can be done on different frequency levels which are usually covered in one treatment. Sometimes it takes more than one for it to be complete. Two more important factors are involved in this process: the removal of a counterforce that attempts to keep us in polarity and the alignment of the keepers.

As we discussed in Chapter 4, part of us stays in unity. Never touched by the fall into separation, this is who we really are. It manifests as an inner force that always strives to return to unity. All of us, with extremely few exceptions, who come to planet Earth in a physical body, carry a counterforce within ourselves that does all it can to undermine every effort we make to transcend polarity and regain unity. Located mostly in the brainstem and the spinal cord, this force is always as strong as we are, so we can never simply overpower it.

At this point, I understand this counterforce as a split aspect of ourselves, or our essence, whatever we want to name it. In Chapter 7 (page 95), I will talk more about split aspects. A very long time ago this particular split aspect has been created and extended over time to almost all humans. It is like a program that turns an aspect of yourself against you.

This seems to be the time for overcoming polarity and experiencing unity while living in a physical body, consequently the tools and insights for integration of this counterforce are now available.

(Somebody trained in lightbody surgery removed mine, but not every lightbody surgeon can do this.) With the brainstem activation, the frequency of the brainstem, and later, the spinal cord, goes way up. When the frequency soars, the counterforce cannot stay and integrates.

At this time, I want to issue a warning. As I discuss in the next chapter, "The Way It Works," RCT is only successful if we allow things to happen. If we try to get rid of this force in our own or somebody else's body, we can cause a lot of damage. The mind and body have to be ready for a change of this magnitude. Doing work like this demands a lot of insight and experience.

One more time: Never attempt this unless you have learned it from somebody experienced. If you think you are skilled enough, at least get supervision from somebody with knowledge and experience.

Once we activate the brainstem and the counterforce integrates, it is no longer present to try and keep us in polarity. This is a tremendous change in life.

Realignment of the keepers has to accompany brainstem activation. Remember that we defined the keepers as the consciousness of the systemic function of the physical body. The keepers are actual beings that come in with us at the time of conception, when we connect to our mother's womb and start building our physical body. They are specialists in their field and they have all the knowledge and experience it takes to do their job and run the body's systems. Their information usually only goes as far as running a body that has been connected to up to the fourth frequency. I don't know why. After the body receives the brainstem activation, the keepers suddenly become confused; they don't seem to know what to do. The connection to the lightbody blueprint appears to initiate such a strong change that they do not have the information to cope with it. Therefore, what shows up after every brainstem activation—usually in the next or one of the following treatments—is the realignment of the keepers, or, as things stand now, the keepers' connection to at least the seven frequencies of the first center.

My friend and lightbody surgeon, Nicolas Guy Ngan, first made me aware of the keepers' confusion, after I had done a few brainstem activations in a training situation at his place in London. If you leave out the alignment of the keepers, it can cause long-term confusion in the body. Over time, more and more of the keepers might figure out what happened and receive the information they need. Others might become upset for a while, and some might even quit and only perform the absolute necessities. Therefore, the whole process runs a lot smoother if the realignment of the keepers is done properly after the activation of the brainstem. Be aware that these things can change. For example, when more people have gone through the brainstem activation, or when the frequency of Earth has risen beyond a certain threshold, this information might become increasingly accessible, and these procedures might happen spontaneously, more often and with greater ease.

The Sixth Frequency: The Activation of the Pineal Gland

To understand the sixth frequency and the activation of the pineal gland, we need to recall everything we talked about in Chapter 4, including our discussion of parallel realities and their re-merging when the frequency rises. This is where the pineal gland comes into play.

Western medicine does not know much about the pineal gland's function. It appears to produce melatonin and be responsible for circadian rhythms in the body. We will learn later that every part of the brain has a physical as well as an energetic role. I do not know any more about the physical function of this gland, but one of its energetic functions is to merge the dimensions or parallel realities.

In this context, it is interesting to look at the anatomy of the pineal gland. The pineal gland is the posterior-most part of the thalamus and about as big as a pea. The thalamus is a paired structure, but the pineal gland is not. Splitting into parts got us into polarity. It is interesting that the pineal gland, which is the structure through which the splits merge again into unity, is one piece.

I suspect that the pineal gland is so small because it has atrophied due to lack of use for thousands of years. The activation of the pineal gland seems to speed up the process of merging the dimensions tremendously. I used to see it take place in seven steps as illustrated below.

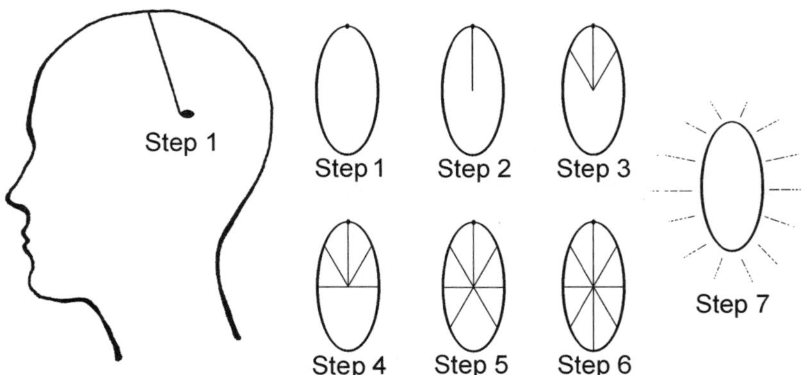

Fig. 5.8. The activation of the pineal gland.

The first step is a beam of white light that extends from the top of the head to the anterior-most part of the pineal gland. Steps 2 through 7 are shown in Figure 5.8. The straight lines in the picture are also beams of white light. In the seventh step, the whole gland becomes white light. Often the activation looks like this but there have also been instances where it looked different.

With every step of the pineal gland activation, a star-tetrahedron field emerges around the body. A star tetrahedron is a geometric structure that consists of two identical tetrahedrons—one tip up and the other tip down. One reaches about two-thirds into the other and is rotated 180 degrees against the first. (Figure 5.9, next page) These star tetrahedrons are generally hard to see because their lines are very thin and faint grey. They include the whole body and end about a hand's width above the head and below the feet.

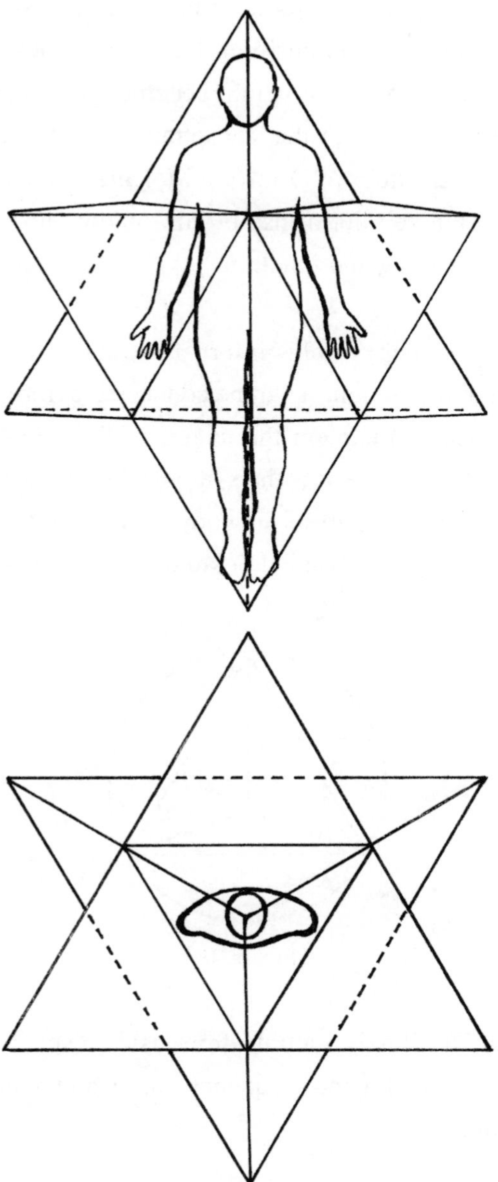

Fig. 5.9. Star tetrahedron as seen from the front and from above.

All seven star tetrahedrons seem to rotate against each other, so that no two are in the same position. I can keep track of about four of them, but then the whole structure becomes so complex that I can no longer distinguish any of the star tetrahedrons from each other. I have studied the teachings of Drunvalo Melchizedek on the star tetrahedrons and they give a lot of useful information, however I remain unsure of their meaning and function.

The sixth frequency holds information about higher-frequency body structure and function. It can be connected before activating the pineal gland. I cannot explain the nature of these higher-frequency functions in detail. I only know the symbols through which they communicate to me, and the part of the body to which they relate. All the symbols shown in this section belong to the sixth frequency.

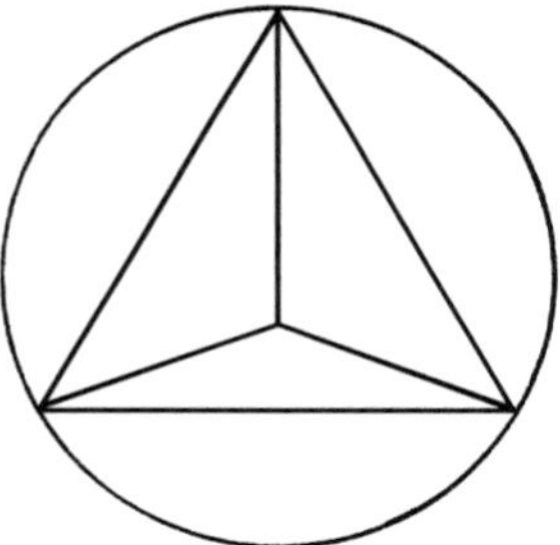

Fig. 5.10.

Figure 5.10. This is a tetrahedron inside a sphere, and it holds the information about higher- frequency cortex and hemisphere structure and function.

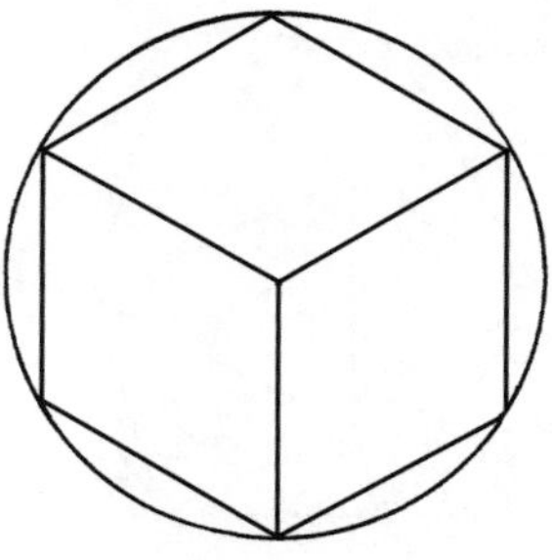

Fig. 5.11.

Figure 5.11. This is a cube inside a sphere, and it holds the information about higher- frequency brainstem structure and function.

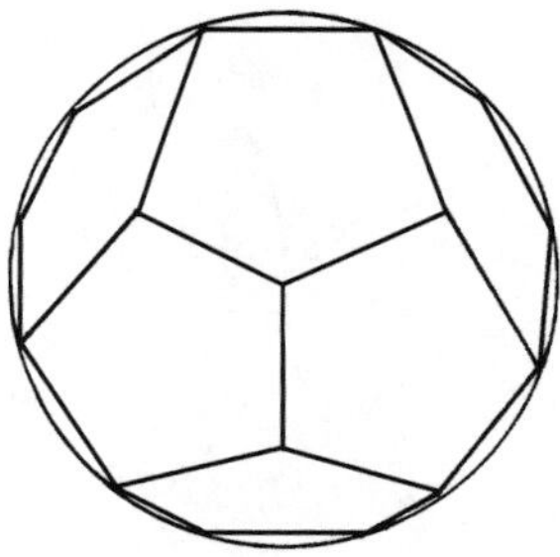

Fig. 5.12.

Figure 5.12. This is a dodecahedron inside a sphere, and it holds the information about higher-frequency bone structure and function.

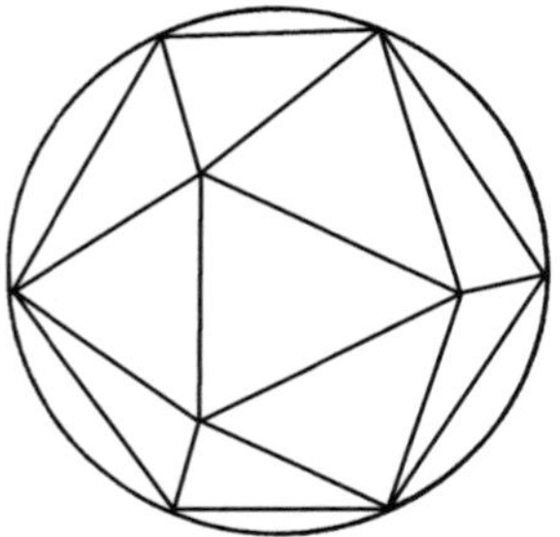

Fig. 5.13.

Figure 5.13. This is an icosahedron inside a sphere, and it holds the information about higher-frequency heart structure and function.

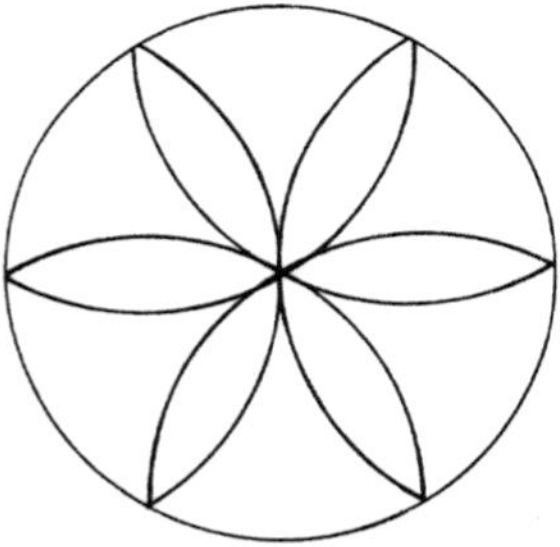

Fig. 5.14.

Figure 5.14. This structure holds the information about higher-frequency organ structure and function.

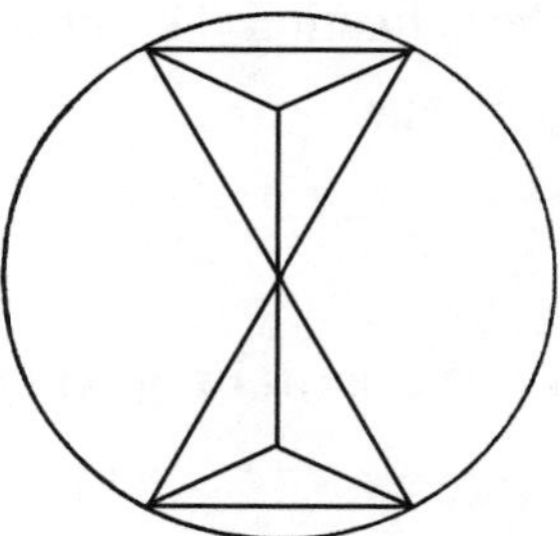

Fig. 5.15.

Figure 5.15. These are two tetrahedrons, tip-on-tip, inside a sphere, and this figure holds the information about merging chakras and qualities

You can see that all these structures are made from the platonic solids and contain all of them. Right now, I don't know what this means.

With few exceptions, brainstem activation has to precede activation of the pineal gland. Some people connect to the sixth frequency before they have the brainstem activation, though I am not clear why. Unlike brainstem activation, which is usually done once and forever, pineal gland activation can be performed several times. In some people, the body wants to connect to this information a number of times. The body seems to use the information that connects through the pineal gland to heal its physical structures as well as the mind.

Generally speaking, after we complete one step of the pineal gland activation, the brain hemispheres and the brainstem want to be connected to the information about their higher-frequency structure and function. I think this is due to the extremely high frequency coming into the brain after the activation. The surrounding parts then have to be upgraded in order to cope.

The Seventh Frequency

Figure 5.16 shows what the seventh frequency looks like to me. Drunvalo Melchizedek calls it the "flower of life." According to Drunvalo and his sacred geometry, it holds complete information about the whole creation.

I don't yet know much about the seventh frequency, however, it appears to hold the information for regenerating lost body parts, such as limbs, organs or teeth. To date I have seen some of this happening, which shows me the body's possibilities, once it has been reminded of them.

Fig. 5.16. The flower of life.

When the seventh frequency connects to the body in a certain way, the energy field explodes and looks like a disc with a diameter of about fifty-to-sixty feet that expands horizontally around the physical body. The expanded field generally does not stay long, maybe a few minutes, and then it shrinks. It looks like what Drunvalo Melchizedek calls the *merkabah.*

Recently I have seen star tetrahedrons emerging around bodies connected to the seventh frequency. These differ from those that appear with the sixth frequency, having thicker lines that are made of bright white light. They can appear around the whole body, as well as any part of the body that becomes connected.

I have seen additional phenomena in conjunction with connections to seventh frequency, but I do not have enough insight into them to be able to talk about them.

About the Frequencies of the Other Centers

The second center feels as if it holds information of a more emotional quality.

The second frequency of this center is what I call an identification release. An identification is a complex structure made out of feelings, thought patterns and belief systems, born out of our interpretation of life experience. When noticing this structure, we think: "This is me." However, it is not us; it is who we think we are. These structures give us the framework to relate to the world. They enable us to understand and be with our experience.

At some point in our evolution, these structures become too narrow. Higher aspects of ourself start to connect more and more to our body and the old systems of relationship and interpretation become too narrow. At this juncture, the body might show these identifications for release. When this happens, I see two spirals of energy around the area of the left and right sides of the coronal suture. Most of the time the left one moves counter-clockwise and the right one clockwise. Then a pulsing occurs in the energy body, as if something is being pushed out of the system.

In many cases, a white, soft, fuzzy energy that seems to come out of the pituitary gland fills the empty spaces after the identification release. This is reminiscent of what I observe in the third frequency, which tends to fill the body after treatments of the emotional system or the release of strange energy. I consider this white and fuzzy energy to be the first frequency of the second center.

I have seen all the seven frequencies of the second center, but cannot yet convey what I observed.

The third center seems to hold information of a more mental quality. I have seen a few frequencies of this center as well, but here, too, I do not know enough to talk about them.

The information of the fourth and higher centers seems to go beyond individuality. Here we seem to connect to information that activates our interconnectedness with all that is. Thus far, I have seen very few people connect to frequencies of the fourth and fifth center.

6

The Way It Works

In the RCT practitioner trainings, I have discovered that each person who learns RCT has his or her own unique way of putting it to work. In this book, I share my personal experience with you, but that does not mean that this is the only way to do RCT. However, the basic structures that I describe always seem to stay the same, and the conditions for RCT to work are also consistently identical. If they are not fulfilled, it does not work.

Chapter Six

The Mechanics of Disconnection and Reconnection: An Example

The information held in the energy body connects through certain interfaces into the physical body. Here the information is translated into impulses that organize matter in the related body part to create perfect body structure and function.

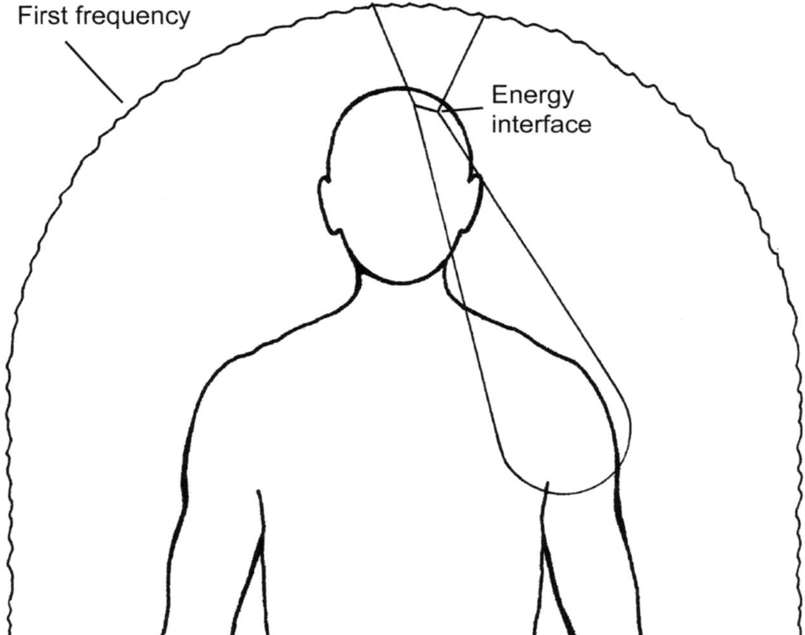

Fig. 6.1. First frequency information about structure and function of the left shoulder connecting through the interface into the physical body.

Figure 6.1 shows an example of how the first frequency connects through the related interface in the brain and so links the body to the information about structure and function of the left shoulder. Just for the illustration, I put the first frequency in there like a bubble around the body.

Let's assume that the person in this illustration now sustains an injury to his left shoulder. In this case, he fell and injured the joint capsule.

If a human body receives a physical impact, this impact gets distributed throughout the body. Every cell and piece of tissue takes on some of the impact, until it is absorbed completely. If the impact is too strong for the body to absorb in this way and the body didn't do anything to protect itself, the energy of the impact would travel through the peripheral nervous system into the spinal cord and then up into the brain and kill the person instantly. The body knows about this hazard and has a way to protect itself against it. At the instant of the impact, the body encloses the impact location in an energetic field that has the shape of a sphere. I call this structure a shock pattern. The energy of the impact is frozen within this energetic sphere and is kept from traveling all over the body, especially from traveling into the central nervous system. The good thing about this is that it keeps the person alive. On the negative side, it keeps him from healing as well. I talk more about this phenomenon in Chapter 12, "Body Protection," on page 156.

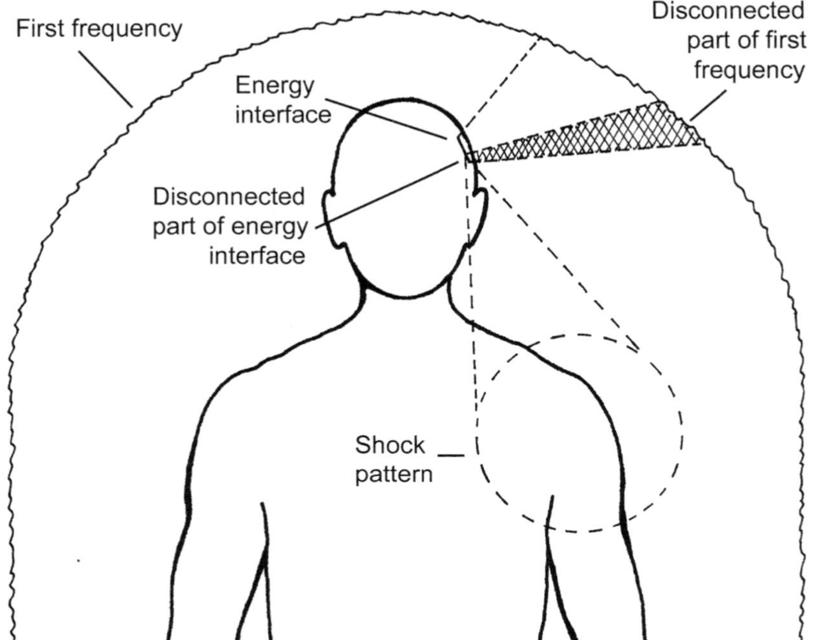

Fig. 6.2. The energy interface has partially disconnected from its original function and has created a shock pattern around the left shoulder.

At the moment of this man's accident, part of an energy interface in his brain disconnects from its original function and starts running an energetic loop that sets up the shock pattern. If you look at Figure 6.2, you can see the sphere made up of dotted lines. This is the shock pattern around the left shoulder. The shaded area in the drawing is the part that disconnected. You can see that the part of the interface that disconnected from its original function is exactly the same one that is setting up the shock pattern around the left shoulder.

Due to the nature of human body structure at this time, these shock patterns, if untreated, remain throughout life. However, once a body's frequency is high enough, the body can release shock patterns by itself.

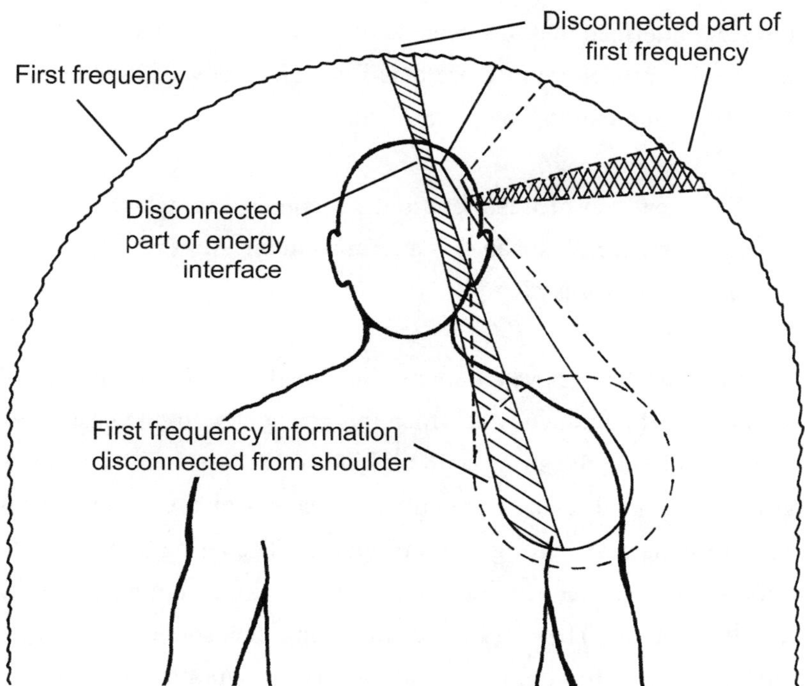

Fig. 6.3. The shock pattern causes a disconnection of parts of first frequency information of structure and function of the left shoulder.

The energetic sphere of the shock pattern pushes part of the information about structure and function out of the shoulder. This means that it disconnects parts of the information about left shoulder structure and function (Figure 6.3). It also causes energetic compression in the shoulder and physical compression in its tissues. The shaded areas in Figure 6.3 show the parts that have disconnected.

Suppose the injured man shows up in the office of a RCT practitioner. The first step in treatment is diagnosis. In RCT, diagnosis consists of finding out which body part or system wants to be reconnected. The therapist asks the body what it wants to have done, and the body shows the interface that has been setting up the shock pattern. I will describe this procedure in more detail in "The Body Consciousness, About Communication," on page 72.

The next step of treatment is the reconnection, which happens through resonance. Resonance is a term from physics that I'll explain through the following example.

Let's say that I have a guitar string tuned to A. The frequency of the tone A is the frequency at which this string can vibrate best. Now I start stimulating the string with all kinds of different frequencies in the form of sound. Once a sound wave reaches our A string, it triggers a response: The string starts to vibrate. The string's response to all these different frequencies is small until I stimulate it with exactly the A that it likes. The vibration of the string then suddenly becomes quite strong. By strong, I mean that the string's vibrational amplitude reaches a maximum that is significantly higher than the ones it reached with all the other frequencies. If no friction or resistance of any kind to the oscillation of the string existed, the amplitude, when stimulated with the right A, would become limitless. This would be the case even if the amplitude of the trigger vibration was infinitely small. This phenomenon is called resonance.

In Figure 6.2, you can see the interface in the brain and the information in the energy body to which it wants to connect. It is the part of the energy interface that has disconnected from its original function in order to set up the shock pattern. The energy interface, the information that wants to connect to the body through it and the connection itself are vibrating on the same distinct frequency.

The therapist's job is to come as close as possible to the interface in the brain, providing exactly this frequency in his or her body. This sets up the resonance effect. The interface and the related part of the energy body both start vibrating at exactly this frequency and, when the amplitude is high enough, the connection crosses over. This procedure usually takes around thirty seconds.

With this, you can see that an RCT treatment does not involve any energy exchange between the therapist and the client. It works strictly through resonance. The impacts that someone feels from an RCT treatment have nothing to do with the therapist. They result solely from information connecting from the person's energy body into his or her physical body.

Once the connection is completed, the body tells the therapist that it has had enough and that it wants his or her hands off. This usually feels as if the body is pushing the therapist's hands out or away from it.

After thirteen years of doing this work, I can say that once the connections are made, they stay. So far, I have never had to do the same connection twice. This does not mean that a therapist will not work on the same part of the body more than once. It simply indicates that something more needs to be done that could not be accomplished in the previous sessions.

With the reconnection of the interface that set up the shock pattern, this interface now connects to its original, or usually, even higher frequency function. This means that it is no longer running the energy loop that was creating the shock pattern. This shock pattern has become non-existent. No release occurred; the body simply stopped creating it.

With the disappearance of the shock pattern, the shoulder generally reconnects by itself to its structural and functional information. In more severe accidents, the injured part of the body has to be reconnected separately most of the time. This treatment will often be next in line after the shock release.

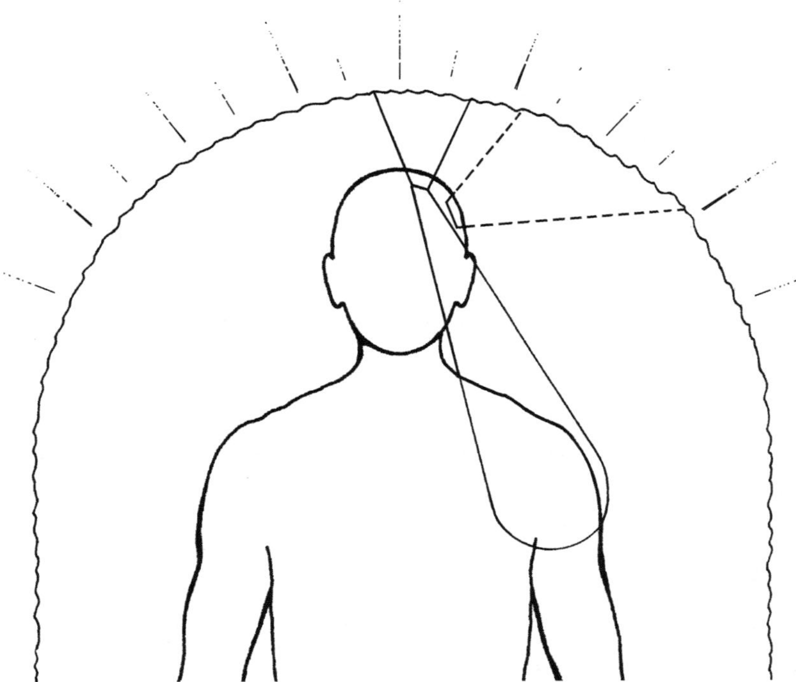

Fig. 6.4. Body after reconnection of the interface that created the shock pattern and the interface for structure and function of the left shoulder.

Figure 6.4 shows the body after the reconnection of the shoulder and the interface that set up the shock pattern. This interface is completely reconnected to the information to which it connected before the accident happened. With the release of the shock pattern, the left shoulder is fully connected to the information about its structure and function. It is now totally healed and functional. In most people, the body is connected to the first frequency only to a very small degree. Therefore, the status before and during the accident will mostly show connections to lower frequencies, and after the treatment connections, to the first frequency. I decided to put the whole drawing into the first frequency, because otherwise it would become too complex to read.

We can give treatments individually or in groups. Usually the body takes about three-to-four weeks of integration before it is ready for another treatment. In the case of acute conditions, the body can take treatments in shorter intervals.

Group treatments are very powerful because of the resonance effect. If the body wants it, the participant can pick up on any treatment that happens in the room. For instance, if a person has the interface for shock reconnected and someone else needs the same thing, he or she can resonate with the information and receive the same healing. Group treatments usually increase in efficiency as more people participate.

We can provide RCT treatments for both groups and individuals long-distance as well in person. One-to-one treatments accomplish the same amount of healing as group sessions, but they may require more sessions.

Chapter Six

The Body Consciousness: About Communication

Remember that in RCT diagnosis, the body tells you what and how to treat. RCT diagnosis comes from communication with the body, especially the parts that hold the information about what has to happen at that moment for a person to heal. This information is generally unavailable to the client's conscious mind. If it were available, the dysfunction would not be there in the first place. I remember a talk I had with a therapist of mine years ago. I had developed a toothache and, in the second session after the pain started, I told her that I had figured out where it came from and why I had it. All she said was: "Oh great. So it is gone now." Damn...

Let's look at this in greater detail.

The body, including every integral component, has a consciousness in and of itself. Each part says to itself: "This is me." Every cell, organ and extremity, every body part, as well as the body as a whole, has this self-awareness. This consciousness knows the status of everything in the body—from electron to organ to totality—at any given time. This is the physical body's consciousness; it is like an entity in itself. Remember that I talked about this briefly when I introduced the first frequency.

Your higher aspects that are not connected to the body at the time of the treatment also have a consciousness. These parts hold the bigger picture of what is going on in you at any given time.

From this point through Chapter 11, I will refer to the unit of

physical and energy body as the "body." If I talk about the energy or the physical body separately, I will make this clear. In RCT diagnosis, you communicate with the unit of physical-body consciousness and everything that is in the energy body. Within the energy body, you listen to your client's higher aspects, and not the aspects that have their source in the interpretation of past experiences. They let you know what has to happen in a treatment.

The body consciousness of anyone you treat knows the complete status of its own physical body at any given time. It also knows everything about the past and possible future, as well as everything in the mind and how it relates to the things it tries to have healed at the time. It knows about the time element and the steps to take to heal and grow. It has a far bigger picture than anything of which the individual or therapist is consciously aware at the time of the treatment.

It will know you as a practitioner, at least at the moment that the person decides to come to you for treatment, if not before that. It knows about your skill and the maximum that the two of you can accomplish when you come together for treatment. This body consciousness will do everything to communicate to you what it wants you to do. It will use any opening in your mind to make you understand what it wants. The desire to communicate can show up in whatever form it takes. You might find a place where your hands feel right; you might see a picture; hear or read words; or you might have the urge to talk about something. All you have to do is to listen.

Most people have more skill in this kind of listening then they think. They perceive the attempts of other consciousnesses to communicate with them as thoughts or feelings showing up in their own minds. The problem many times is that they see these messages as something that their own minds have produced, and so they do not pay any attention to them. Especially since I have been training people in RCT, I have observed that most of these perceptions come from communication with other consciousnesses, particularly if someone has set his mind to listen.

If you wish to enhance your ability to recognize energetic perception, it is helpful to take these messages as something real. This will enable you to explore your own abilities in this area. If you throw these messages out, judging them as unreal the moment they occur, you will have nothing left to explore. To determine whether the messages are valid communications or something from your own inner dialogue, you must give them a chance and initially consider them real.

One day a man came to my practice complaining that he was hallucinating. He said that he had already seen a doctor who had put him on psycho-pharmaceuticals. The medication had helped for a while but had not felt good and he was looking for another solution. One look at him made it clear to me that he had well-developed energetic perception and was able to perceive things that other people cannot.

He told me about the things he could see, and I asked, "What's the problem? I can see the same things."

He began to understand that nothing was wrong with him. He just had one of his senses developed that is still sleeping in most people. He left my practice a happy man.

In my experience, there is no such thing as hallucination. Some people simply see things that are present on different energetic planes. Besides these senses coming online naturally, drugs and extreme stress can activate this kind of perception. Some people are aware of these senses for energetic perception and so they "hallucinate" naturally.

The tricky part, as we already mentioned, is that the body consciousness almost always holds a bigger picture about what is going on and what needs to happen than you or your client can comprehend at the time. Therefore, you might not understand why the body is showing you certain places to treat or is communicating certain pictures or words. In order to follow the advice of the body, you need to understand that you are not the one that knows what needs to happen. (Please do not forget that by "body," I mean the energy body and the physical body as a unit.)

Let me give you a simple example. Let's say you are treating a person with an old scar in the lower right abdomen from an appendix removal years ago. Scars contract over time and, with this contraction, pull on the area's connective tissue. This causes an imbalance in the biomechanics of the pelvis and the tension is transferred, through the connective tissue, all over the body. You even find it in the bones of the skull and the brain.

Now, this is your client and he is asking for treatment. If you scan the body for information, you might find all these secondary effects from the scar and you can treat them one after another. This will not only take dozens of treatments, but will also limit their effect because the tension remains from the scar pulling on the tissues. If you ask the body what to do, it might simply tell you to work on the area of the right, lower abdomen, and there you go. With the release of the tension from the scar, all the problems it caused will disappear and this may require just one treatment.

A woman in her sixties came to me because she had been suffering from a constant headache for about thirty years. All I could see in the treatment was a little baby in her belly. The only thing that I felt I should do was gently communicate this picture to her. She started crying instantly and confessed that she had had an abortion many years ago. This did the job. Her headache disappeared and never came back.

As far as I know, the Catholic Church talks about seven sacraments. You can think of them in whatever way you want. However, I saw that one of these sacraments, confession, is a real power that was present in that moment and this was enough to let the healing happen.

These examples demonstrate clearly that treatments are most effective when the therapist just listens to the body and follows its advice. Often you will not be able to understand why the body asks certain things of you, but this is not important at all. It is only important that you listen and then do what the body requests.

For this reason, I advise all my students never to visualize anything actively while they diagnose and treat. This kind of visualization can limit what the therapist sees, feels and understands at the time. Moreover, as we just explained, the therapist most likely does not have as much information about what the client needs as the client's body consciousness and its higher aspects. Active visualization can therefore limit the outcome of a treatment to what the therapist is able to understand at the given time.

How can we learn to listen to the body?

Most people who do energy work, whether they are beginners or professionals, push their energy body out towards or into the object they want to perceive. From what I have seen so far, this does not work well for two main reasons.

First, nobody likes you breaking into his or her house. People prefer to be asked for permission to come in. They also want to be the ones who open the door. I consider it a matter of basic integrity not to push energy into another person's field. Unfortunately, most energy-work teachings that I have seen teach this kind of energetic perception.

Second, if you have your energy in another person, everything you think and feel in this moment will impact this person. It manipulates his energy body.

I have learned just to let the other person know that I am there. Then I get centered in myself and listen. This is like an invitation for the body to talk and, believe me, every body wants to do this. The information I need, nothing more or less, shows up inside me. This has nothing to do with empathy, through which I feel in my body what others feel in theirs. I have played with this, but found it to be too much of a strain. I don't need it to communicate with the body.

In RCT, we do not scan the body for information. We are just there and allow the body to relate to us whatever it considers necessary. It requires some trust to believe that you truly get the information you need for treatment. However, once you see it work consistently, trust develops quickly.

To communicate successfully in this way, you must be able to create a quiet space inside yourself. The information that comes in can be extremely subtle and too much internal noise might prevent you from hearing it. You cannot calm your mind by trying to shut it up. This only makes things worse. Instead, just be with whatever is inside, without reacting to it in any way. This withdraws your creative power from the noise and the mind then starts to calm down. This exercise works best when your goal is simply to be with what is, rather than to calm down the mind. The more you do this, the more you will be able to create this quiet inner space within a short time.

The next requirement for this kind of listening is the ability to pull your energy body in until it ends at the surface of your skin. Don't pull it in any further, because then you suck in the energy of the other person. This is a lot easier to learn than most people think. Retracting your energy body like this allows the information to come in by itself.

Some people perceive through their chakras, which I think is limiting. Certain chakras have affinities to certain qualities, and so will communicate with these more easily than with others. However, when I listen, I open my whole being for the information to come in. This is like using my whole energy body as a resonator. You can go even deeper than this. You can become one with what- or whomever is with you, and then you go beyond perception.

Perception implies that you see yourself as separate from what you perceive. For this reason, perception has a need for interpretation. If you take a closer look at this, you see that it means that there are as many interpretations or truths as there are people.

When you allow yourself to unify with what is, you will know. This knowing usually occurs in a way that words cannot communicate. How do you know that love exists? You know because you have been there. Can you communicate its nature with words? It is hard to do. All you can find are symptoms of love, but they are just aspects of it, not love itself. You might radiate it when you talk about it and so awaken this knowing in others. Then the verbal communication can serve as a bridge to something indescribable.

Experience from the trainings has shown that the body will communicate a first option. If you are not able to pick it up, it will go for a second or third option down the line, until you get what the body is asking you to do. You will only know that you are treating the first option if you have somebody there who can give you feedback on this.

If you give someone a series of treatments and you look back at the sequence of what you treated, often you will understand more about what the body did and why.

As long as you are not initiated into second frequency, you will connect the information directly through the part of the body that wants treatment. In this case, it is sufficient to know the area where that part is. For example, the body shows you an area right below the solar plexus. Here you find abdominal muscles, connective tissue, maybe parts of the stomach, the duodenum and the large intestine. Further back, you find the pancreas and maybe parts of the kidneys and the spine. You don't have to know exactly what the body wants. When you provide the treatment, whatever needs to be connected will be addressed. Once your energetic capacity for practicing RCT is high enough, it no longer matters whether you know where to treat.

Wherever the treatment needs to go, it goes. However, I strongly recommend to all my students that they keep the structure of diagnosis and treatment at least for a number of years, even if they don't truly need it anymore. RCT has very little structure, and it has proven helpful to keep that little bit until you are fully comfortable to drop it.

If you work through the interfaces, it is not important to know what the body wants to have connected. You just treat and then you try to read what happens during the session. The efficiency of your treatment is completely independent of your ability to read this. The information is just for your patients to get feedback about their treatment. Most people who start their RCT practice do not have much initial ability to read what happens in their sessions. However, over time, their capacity to do this develops more and more.

You must understand that the physical-body consciousness has personality and character, and with this, its own way of looking at things and interpreting them. For example, I had a client who had just undergone triple-bypass surgery in which the surgeons took blood vessels out of her left thigh and replaced damaged coronary arteries with them. The heart and the chest healed well, but the left thigh did not want to heal at all. When I was asked to help and I connected to the body, the left thigh started talking to me. It was extremely upset. "How dare they do this to me—cut me open, remove blood vessels and put them where they don't belong!" It was so angry that it refused to heal.

Then I told the body that it was basically right, but that it might want to look at the fact that the heart was really in trouble and that the only way to fix it at this time was this kind of surgery. Otherwise, the whole body might not be around any more. This did the job and the leg started healing.

If you don't have any experience in working with the body consciousness, you might think that I am seriously exaggerating in this little example. Let me assure you that this was exactly the way it went, and I have seen things like this happen many times.

Bypassing the Conscious Mind

In this section, I want to talk about one of the most important features of RCT, one that is largely responsible for its spectacular effectiveness: It bypasses the conscious mind.

As I see it, healing and evolution are the same thing. When I talk about evolution, I mean that you remember more of whom you really are. On a structural level, it means that more of your essence is connecting to your body.

I use the words "essence" and "personality" in this book in particular ways. Personality is who we think we are and essence is who we really are. These two are not necessarily remotely similar in the same person. Earlier, I talked about the fact that we have forgotten who we are, that most of us have become alienated from our essential nature. As I define it, healing connects a higher aspect of ourselves into the physical body, and this higher aspect becomes not only conscious but also available to us again. With this, we can understand that every step in the healing process leads us into something unknown.

It seems to me that the conscious mind's job is to keep the status quo. Staying with what we know and can interpret provides a certain state of balance. The conscious mind resists everything that is unknown or unfamiliar and threatens this mental and emotional balance. The more that you can let go and trust, the more you can experience strong changes consciously. The more that you have experiences that turn out well, the more you can suspend this protective function of the conscious mind.

On the other hand, I also see this function's importance. It is a part of the body protection and kicks in whenever the input of information and emotions threatens to overwhelm you.

If the healing process had to go through the conscious mind, it might be arduous or at times even impossible. In an RCT treatment, most of what wants to connect is higher aspects of your self. These seem alien to the conscious mind and, generally, it won't allow them in. At best, it allows tiny parts in and tests them thoroughly for compatibility. This could take an awesome amount of time.

RCT works with information that is beyond space and time, which is one of the reasons that it can bypass the conscious mind. In these realms, you are everything with which you have ever identified at the same time. Whatever you will become within your path of evolution is also already there. The only question is if or when you are going to experience it. For this to happen, the information needs to be connected all the way down into your physical body. The wisdom in your body consciousness seems to know this and, in my experience, warmly welcomes the connections with your higher aspects. The conscious mind alone puts up the main barriers.

Once these higher aspects are connected in a treatment, the physical body and unconscious parts of the mind change quickly. The conscious mind catches up over time. I often get this feedback from people who have gone through some changes within their minds during the course of treatment: "I feel different. I don't know what it is, but it feels good."

With very few exceptions, the process of RCT completely bypasses the conscious mind of the person who is treated. This is one of the main reasons it is so effective and fast.

What Allows the Reconnections to Happen?

Once you complete the diagnosis, you know what the body is asking you to do. You know the body part that wants to be treated. As I mentioned earlier, this is only important when the body asks you to perform the reconnection directly through that body part. If you can work through an interface, you don't have to know in advance what the body wants to have treated. Two conditions must be met for this kind of treatment to work. First, you must not manipulate. On a structural level, this means that you need to pull back your energy field to the surface of your skin. We discussed this previously in the section on listening (see page 72). Second, in the moment of treatment, you must allow yourself to become one with the person you treat. Your skill in fulfilling these two conditions determines your effectiveness in RCT treatments.

In the trainings I have conducted, I have seen people whose ability to allow this connection to happen is so strong, that even for first frequency connection directly through the body part, they don't have to know what the body wants to have treated. It does not matter where they put their hands. The connections that the body wants just happen.

Let's look into this more deeply. In RCT, you can connect higher frequency information from people's energy bodies into their physical bodies. In other words, you connect higher aspects of people's selves into their bodies.

Remember that in the higher frequency realms, space and linear time do not exist. If you connect to this part of yourself, you see that your energy field does not have boundaries. All of you is everywhere, is one with all that is. This does not mean that you won't have a feeling for who you are. I have seen that the closer you come to this experience, the clearer your sense of self becomes. However, things can also be quite different. When you connect to higher aspects of yourself, you might come to a place where you feel that you are totally present. In this place, past and future do not exist; everything is right now. Mental and physical dysfunction, pain, sadness or similar feelings are gone; only overflowing joy remains. As I have seen it, everybody can allow himself to connect to this place at any time.

The information that we connect into the body with RCT is about our essence, which is one with everything. To facilitate this connection, you have to be there, in this place of unity. You can go to this place of oneness just with yourself, or you can connect in this way to another person or any kind of living being.

Learning to allow this kind of connection to another person is one of the exercises in the introductory class. I am frequently asked: "How do you do this? Don't you have to be extremely evolved to be able to go there?" and so on. The nice thing about this experience is that you cannot **do** it. You can only allow it to happen.

The concept and experience of separation are more alien to your real nature than anything else that you can imagine. To maintain separation, it has to be created constantly; otherwise, it collapses and you become who you really are. In other words, your memory of your real self will be restored. Your real self is always present; it is the only thing that is real. You don't have to make any effort to get to it, because it is who you already are. All you have to do to connect to your real self is relax. Believe me. It is that easy.

As we have learned, the conscious mind has the job of maintaining stability by maintaining the status quo. Therefore, every action based on the conscious mind's involvement interferes with your real self and prevents the connection from happening. This does not mean that this kind of action is wrong. However, it does mean that you cannot connect to your essence in this way. You can learn ways to act from higher aspects of your self, but this is something that I do not want to discuss here. Right now, it is just important to know how to connect to who you really are, and that this cannot happen as long as you are actively trying to do it.

Total communication is an aspect of our higher self. If you connect to a person and simply relax and don't do anything, you will go as naturally to the place of oneness with this person as water flows downhill. More than three years of training people have shown me that it really works this way.

What we usually call the energy field has boundaries; its layers extend only a certain distance out. This aspect of the energy field correlates to personality, and this is what we pull in for the duration of the treatment. Your real self or essence does not have any boundaries, nor does its corresponding energy field. You are everywhere and connected to everything all the time.

Personality is subject to frequent changes. It is most important to have a personality that is stable and strong, because it is the vehicle through which your essence expresses itself here in the world, as long as you do not fully recognize who you are, It is helpful to honor your personality, but not to identify with it, because this can make it too hard to connect with your essence.

Doing, in the way most of you understand it today, is an aspect of personality. Because you want to make connections to higher aspects of yourself, doing that comes from personality will be in the way. This is another reason why you have to learn to pull your energy field back to the surface of your skin for the duration of the diagnosis and treatment. You do not want this involved in the process.

Intention

In this subchapter, I will try to explain, how you can put the information about the diagnosis and treatments to work. Remember that in my earlier discussion of diagnosis, I described the need to pull your energy field in to listen. In addition, to do the treatment, you have to allow yourself to become one with the person you treat.

Let me now try to explain what I mean by intention. When you set an intent, you give your mind a direction. For example, when you sit in a group of people, you can decide to put your attention on one particular person. Similarly, when you are in a concert, you can set your intent on listening to the music, observing the musicians or just being with your own thoughts and feelings. In all these examples, you choose the contents of your attention, or to whom you want to open yourself. When you give one person in a room full of people 100 percent of your attention, all the others in the room cease to exist for you for awhile. This way of using intent does not necessarily involve pushing your energy out towards or into the object of your attention. You can be with whomever or whatever you prefer and stay in yourself at the same time.

In the same way, from the moment you start an RCT session, you always keep an aspect of your energy field pulled in. Once you elect to give only one person your attention, you will perceive information only from this person and from nobody and nothing else. Intent, as I use it here, is like a command that you give to yourself, like a direction that you give your mind. Once you give the command, your energy body obeys and does exactly what you ask.

To utilize intent in the way I train practitioners to use it, you must know that once you set your intent, whatever you intend just happens, without you doing anything about it. If you set your intent and then use your energy to make sure that you get the desired result, you actually interfere with it. Once you establish your intent, you have to trust that things are unfolding in exactly the way that you created. The more you trust that it actually works just like this, the less you will interfere, and the more your intent can unfold in the best way. This is a little bit like asking God to do something for you. Once you ask, you trust that it is really going to happen. If it does not come about, it could be that your request is not in everyone's best interest. You can then consider yourself lucky that it did not occur.

When you ask God for help with something, you trust that it is going to happen in a way that is best for everyone. You know that God's understanding of things is a lot broader than yours, so you don't tell Him how to act. You also don't attempt to help, because to do so might limit the outcome to your understanding, which is not anywhere as complete as God's.

To understand and practice the use of intent that I just described is a major key to being able to practice RCT. In my experience, using intention this way is as far as you can go actively. Whatever happens after you set your intent is not your business anymore. You are just there and allow whatever wants to happen to unfold. Trust seems to be the major quality that allows this process to take place.

This way of working with your mind goes against almost everything that Western society teaches. In the Western paradigms for work and accomplishment, you generally learn that if you don't make something happen, nothing is going to happen. In practicing RCT, you will learn that things only take place if you allow them to come about. and do not attempt to interfere or make them happen. Again, to set your intent is as far as you can go actively.

If you have never taught your mind to function this way, the results of your first applications of this power might be a bit rusty. Your mind may seem to operate like a pack of dogs that has never been trained. They are accustomed to do whatever they want. If you now decide that they should do what you want, they will quite likely laugh at you and not take you seriously. It might therefore take some firmness in the beginning, but soon they will feel your determination, and know that they have to follow this new regimen.

In RCT training, you learn how to use intention. In the first series of classes, you learn all the steps that together make a complete treatment. The first step is to use your intent to pull in your energy field, so that it ends exactly at the surface of your skin. Most people are utterly surprised that this really happens when they simply set the intent for it. To do the diagnosis, you set your intent for listening. This means, that you just listen to the body that you want to diagnose and nothing else. Listening includes a specific and clear question to the body: "What is it you want me to treat?" Once you have the diagnosis, you set your intent for treatment. This means that you allow yourself to become one with the person you treat. All three intents—to pull in the energy field, to listen and to be in treatment mode—stay until the treatment is over. After the diagnosis. the listening mode no longer holds an inherent question about what the body wants you to treat. Instead, you listen for information about what happens in the body during the treatment. You learn this step when you gain the ability to treat and listen at the same time. After the treatment is complete, you return to your normal state. This means that none of the intents you set for diagnosis, listening and treatment remain active.

Using intent in the way I just described is a very powerful tool not just for RCT but also for other aspects of your life. However, I am not going to talk about these, and will limit my self to the application of intent to RCT treatments.

The most important thing to understand about setting intent is that this is all the action you need to take. Whatever happens after you set your intent for the different modes of diagnosis and treatment is completely out of your control. After you clearly set your intent, it is vital that you just relax and be with whatever happens. This relaxation requires trust: first, that your intent will really unfold in just the right way, and second, that whatever happens as a consequence will be completely in alignment with divine order. It is my understanding and experience that as long as you follow the rules for RCT practice, you will not be able to cause any harm, because you do not make things happen or manipulate in any way. You simply serve as a catalyst for these connections between a higher aspect of your client's self and physical body.

The Male and Female Principles

I recently became aware of another facet of RCT that I want to share to help give you a better understanding of the way RCT works.

Remember that in Chapter 4 we talked about the fall from unity and the way back. Let us assume that the way that we generally experience men and women does not exist in unity. Let's say that instead, these two are actually a perfect unit. The male principle is the active part of that union—it makes things happen—while the female principle is passive—it allows things to happen. Contemporary Western culture is extremely male-oriented and consequently puts a lot more value on the active, male principle than on the passive, female one. I say this to help you understand that neither principle is better than the other. They are one unit that perceives itself within polarity as two different aspects, male and female.

The fact that somebody shows up as a man within polarity does not mean that his mind is completely male. Every man has female aspects in himself and vice versa.

Some interesting questions arise from the fall out of unity: "How could this happen? What could have possibly been the first impulse that led to an action so far from our real nature?"

I cannot answer these questions, but one thing appears clear to me. The fall out of unity was initiated by the male principle. Only the masculine, active aspect of the mind can do something like this. How could the impulse for separation possibly have entered the female mind? If it did, how could this passive principle possibly have translated it into action?

The moment the male aspect decided to separate, it lowered the frequency of the unit and the male and female aspects split into man and woman. Naturally, the woman could do nothing about this and she just had to watch it happen. This was a shock for her, a shock that seems to be so deeply ingrained that it impacts her strongly to the present day. For example, one of women's biggest and most common fears in intimate relationships is being left behind.

The male aspect now played out the game of separation in all its aspects and varieties. The female part of the mind has no business in this whatsoever; it is passive and simply not structured to do something like this. This does not mean that women cannot play this game. They play it well, but only if they use the male or active aspect of their minds.

Chapter Six

Western culture is highly male-oriented. We do things because we can and not because they make any sense. Little remains that has any intrinsic value. We honor the kind of strength that makes things happen or in other words the strength and the willingness to be the biggest bully in the playground. War, pollution, hunger and abuse are symptoms of a culture that elevates the male side of the mind to the extreme and is completely out of balance.

Interestingly, the stronger the masculine imbalance grows, the more men crave women. They have a deep longing for female presence and contact in their lives that they cannot explain. In its darkest expressions, men try to satisfy this longing forcefully. Rape, enforced prostitution and so on are its most common consequences.

In cultures that are (or have been) serious about finding a way back into unity, we can find a deep honoring of the female principle in all areas of life. Somehow, the men become aware, that their mindset created separation. They also see that the female perspective and style of action are going to help them back into unity.

From the Lord's prayer, "Thy will be done," to *Zazen*, you will find that the passive principle allows the events and conditions that will finally reconnect you to unity to take place. From the female mind comes the ability to be completely passive, simply to let life unfold. Naturally, it is easier for women to understand and walk this way than for men. Things got out of balance from the male side of the mind, so they have to come back into balance through the female side. Once balance is restored, they can recognize that they are and have always been one.

The time in polarity has led to all kinds of emotional wounds between the two genders that are probably just a continuation of the two original ones. Women blame men for instigating the fall out of unity, and men feel guilty for having done just that. Forgiveness seems to be needed (see "About Forgiveness," page 120) to allow these wounds to heal once and forever.

We find plenty of drama and comedy in the ways that men and women try to approach each other. They are fundamentally one, so they will always try to get back together, no matter how. However, their minds are structured so differently, that they literally have no way of understanding each other. Fortunately, love does not really need this kind of understanding.

For a man, the way a woman functions is about the strangest thing on the planet, and vice versa. Here, then, we find nearly perfect conditions to facilitate acceptance and surrender, because only acceptance and surrender can make an intimate relationship between a man and a woman work. Step by step, each must give up his/her identity and merge with the other. Men tend to feel that they have much more to lose than women. They therefore can be more fearful about intimacy. Fortunately, men have women right next to them, and they can learn from them.

When a man and a woman become one, they unleash a beautiful power. They create something new every time this happens. On the physical level, it can express as a child, as new life, but it is not limited to this. When the minds of a man and a woman merge, everything is born anew in every moment of their lives. This is one of the most exquisite things I have ever experienced.

The male side of the mind can do things independently. It remembers and uses its inherit strength by itself. Thus, Western culture greatly honors the lone fighter. In contrast, I love the movie *Apollo 13*, because it offers a prime example of the power of relationship. The astronauts and ground team work together to master a critical task: the rescue of three men on a failed mission to the moon. They succeed because everybody puts in 100 percent of what they have to give.

Besides facilitating the restructuring of the body and mind, Reconnective Therapy profoundly supports and accelerates the way back to unity. Consequently, it is a wonderful balance of the male and the female principles. The male aspect comes in first, when you set the intention. After this, you can only proceed if you completely switch over to the female side of your mind and allow whatever wants to happen.

RCT utilizes the gift we hold for each other, and this is to remind each other of who we really are. RCT only works within the most intimate form of relationship: two people becoming one.

7

The Interconnection of Mind and Body and the Healing of the Mind

The Basic Structure of the Mind and Its Interconnection with the Body

When I use the term "mind," I refer to all possible thoughts and feelings on all frequency levels, i.e., not only the superficial daily chatter of the lower-frequency mind, but also insights, ideas and emotions of very high-frequency origin.

The mind's basic function, as I understand it today, is to create. Don't forget that our mind is a lot more than the content and activity of which we are consciously aware. This creative function is always active, whether we know it or not. If we accept this as a fact, our lives will change drastically in many ways. If the mind is primarily creative, it means that no one else is responsible for anything that happens to us. We have always created our own experiences and others have just stepped in to help us fulfill what we created. Most of us, however, do not have conscious access to many parts of our mind, which makes things tricky. We often create things that the conscious mind does not really appreciate. If we are not aware of how the mind works, we find it hard to understand how life works and why things happen to us the way they do. We start blaming others or God, and end up feeling frustrated and resigned.

If we understand the creative function of the mind, this knowledge alone can set us free. We can understand our entire world as a mirror of what goes on in our minds. With this, we have a new way of seeing ourselves and letting things heal.

Remember that we talked about certain aspects of the human experience in Chapter 4. Within this context, it is important to understand that the experience of polarity on planet Earth is the way it is because we think and believe that it is this way. If I look at the table under my laptop, I know that this is not a table. In fact, people see and experience a structure like this as a table and name it accordingly by collective agreement. It works like this with everything that we experience here in polarity or, in other words, separation. Humankind is dreaming the dream of separation collectively. If we look at humankind's history, it seems like more of a nightmare than a happy dream.

If you find yourself in a nightmare and believe that it is real, you try to deal with the situation in the best way that you can. If you know you are dreaming, you try hard to wake up as quickly as possible. If you think you are awake, you take everything as real and try to work the system within the parameters of the dream. You derive a great benefit from understanding that you are dreaming. You start to withdraw your creative energy from the dream, because you already know, or at least have the suspicion, that it is one. The more you withdraw your creative energy from the dream, the more it collapses, because you do not feed it any more. With this, space opens up inside your mind for some of the real you to connect and to change your reality from there.

It is critically important to understand this in order to understand how RCT functions. With RCT, we work directly on the interfaces where the mind connects to the body. When we connect higher frequencies, or in other words, a person's higher aspects into the body, the person starts to experience this higher aspect of him or herself in life. The person then automatically creates a different experience that expresses what has been connected.

As we consider this, we start to comprehend the basic structure of RCT more deeply. We see that for the mind to heal, we do not have to engage in any kind of processing of past experiences or issues through the conscious mind. The mind begins to create a different experience simply by reconnecting to its own higher aspects. We also get a more profound understanding of why and how this kind of reconnection bypasses the conscious mind.

I experience the mind and physical body as a unit. The mind is not in one place and the physical body in another, sometimes connected and sometimes not—a situation described by the term psychosomatic. I see the physical body as an expression of the mind in the three-dimensional realm. The mind rules everything that is going on in the physical body. Every physical dysfunction is a creation of the mind, as is physiological well-being.

If we look at the way information connects in RCT, we can see that we always treat the physical body and the mind as a unit. If you have an RCT treatment and get rid of a back pain, for example, the structures in the mind that created this have been healed as well. We can treat the back pain by reconnecting the structure of the physical body, and from there, the mind. Alternatively, we can treat it by reconnecting the mind directly through the emotional and mental system. The outcome is the same. Our procedure depends on what the body shows us to do.

An Example of the Mechanics of Disconnection and Reconnection

Now that we have a concise picture of the basic function of the mind and its interconnection with the physical body, I want to provide a look at how things work on a structural level. To do this, I'll describe a typical treatment scenario, beginning with small details and then enlarging the scope to include as much of the whole picture as I can. I will keep the description relatively simple, so that we gain sufficient understanding but don't get lost in too many details.

Let's consider a child who grew up in harmony and joy until

she was about four years old, at which point a close family member sexually abused her. This experience was too overwhelming for her to integrate or digest.

A self-protective mechanism in the psyche steps in when something like this happens and does three main things:

1. The victim's energy body leaves her physical body and gets as far away as it can. This insures that the injured person will feel as little as possible from the whole event.

2. It splits the part of the person that has experienced the trauma from the rest of the body. In this case, part of the little girl remains on the energetic plane with all the memory, the feelings and her interpretation of the event. The split also makes sure that over time the conscious mind will not have any access to the memory of the event.

We can understand how this works if we look into the sleep state. In sleep, our energy body moves out of our physical body and is only connected through what looks like a silvery cord. In this state, we can have all kinds of experiences. We call them dreams when we remember them. Most of us do not recall most of our dreams, because we do not know how to bring our conscious minds over the threshold of sleep. Usually we remember only the events that happen shortly before we awaken.

This resembles the split. The split usually does not occur instantly, but becomes more complete over time. As it does so, the connection of the split part to the body becomes fainter and, in our example, our little girl has less and less access to the memory this part of her holds, until eventually it is totally inaccessible. Later on in life, when her frequency starts to rise again, this part of her might come closer, and then she might start feeling the old emotions again. The closer this part comes, the stronger the emotions will be. Split aspects can never ultimately detach from the person from whom they separate.

3. The self-protective mechanism of the mind tries to make sure that something like this can never occur again.

In our example, someone close to the child perpetrated the abuse. From now on, the girl will have a mental program that triggers whenever somebody comes too close. This program might say that closeness or intimacy with another human being equals danger. The sense of danger that she feels may become so strong that it feels life threatening. If someone comes even closer and the sense of endangerment grows, the child—and later on, the adult—might feel so threatened that she becomes enraged and violently attacks the person who is the perceived threat.

It takes some experience to determine whether our feelings are triggered by patterns of self-protection or are an appropriate response to the current situation. If we look into the life of a person with an unhealed structure like this, we will most likely find an inability to maintain an intimate relationship. At some point, the self-protecting mechanism triggers and the person disallows closeness. The mental system sets up this part of the self-protective mechanism.

These mechanisms are not something bad. If they were not available, our little girl would probably have died at the time of the event or shortly after, or would have ended up in a mental institution.

Let's now look at how the body sets this up on the structural level.

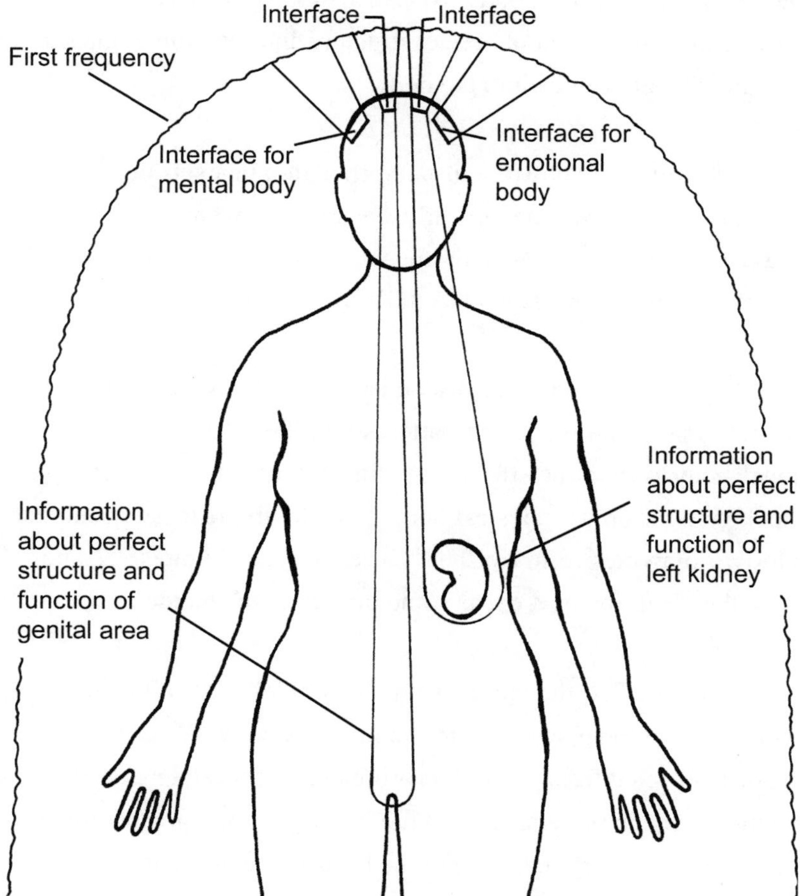

Fig. 7.1. Interfaces for the emotional and mental body as well as for the first frequency information about kidney and genital structure and function.

Figure 7.1 shows the interfaces that are going to set up the emotional and mental shock patterns in the body. The interface on the far-left side of the head is for the emotional body and the one on the far-right side is for the mental body. In their healthy state as shown here, they have a different job. Let's say they connect certain emotional and mental qualities into the body. We can also see the interfaces that connect the information about perfect structure and function of the genital area and the left kidney into the body.

I do not know how the instant protection that sets up at the moment of shock works energetically, because I have never observed it. I have only seen the long-term impact, which is what I will describe, and what we will commonly see in RCT practice.

Figure 7.2 shows the disconnection of the emotional and the mental system and the shock patterns that the interface for the emotional body is creating. In 7.3, we find the effects of the emotional shock patterns on the physical body. I had to divide these phenomena into two drawings to make them easier to read. Figures 7.2 and 7.3 show the condition as it exists some time after the incident.

In Figure 7.2, the interface on the very left side of the head connects the emotional system into the physical body. We can see that it has disconnected from parts of its original function and has created the emotional shock patterns around the left kidney and genital area. The interface on the very right side of the head connects the mental system into the physical body. The shaded parts show the disconnections. The drawing shows that it has also disconnected from parts of its original function. This part is running an energy loop that creates the mental patterns that are set to make sure that the traumatic event will not recur with anyone else.

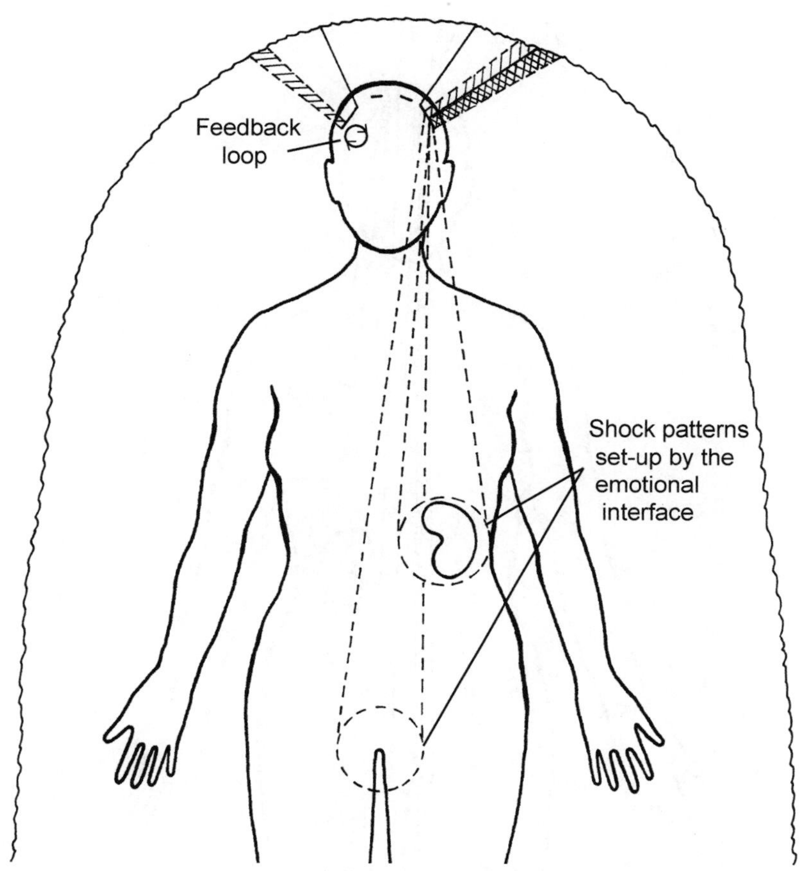

Fig. 7.2. The emotional and mental interfaces have disconnected from parts of their original function. The shaded areas show the information that has disconnected. The disconnected part of the emotional interface has set a shock pattern around the kidney and the genitals. The disconnected part of the mental interface has created a feedback loop.

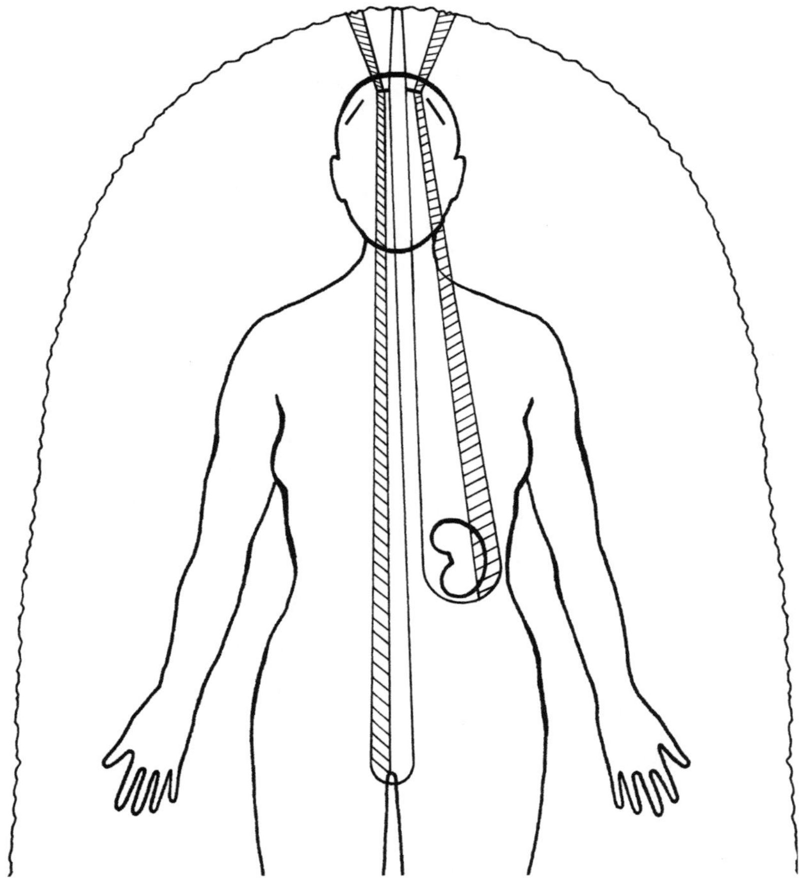

Fig. 7.3. Emotional shock disconnects the kidney and the genitals from parts of the information about their structure and function. The shaded areas represent the disconnected information.

In Figure 7.3, we can see how the emotional shock affects the left kidney and genital area and disconnects them from parts of the information about their structure and function. The shaded parts show the disconnections.

The emotional shock patterns work in basically the same way as the physical ones (see "Body Protection" on page 156). They lock the energy of an emotional impact into an energetic capsule that surrounds the areas of the impact. This compresses the body part energetically as well as physically. They also push part of the information about structure and function (in our case) out of the kidney and the genital area (Figure 7.3). Over time, all this usually leads to problems. It is the same mechanism that I explained in Chapter 6, "The Mechanics of Disconnection and Reconnection: An Example" on page 64 in relation to the physical trauma.

As soon as the shock happens, a part of the interface for the emotional body instantly disconnects from its original job and runs something like an energy loop. This encapsulates the energy generated by the event and creates the split we have been discussing. It also disconnects the conscious mind from the memory of the event. Additionally, it puts a shock pattern around the parts of the physical body that have been directly involved in the abuse, in our case the whole genital area (Figure 7.2). The shaded areas show the parts that have disconnected from the energy body, as we saw in the drawings in Chapter 6. Then it puts a shock pattern around the part of the physical body that is going to take on the emotions involved in the event, in our case the left kidney.

Let me explain the latter. If something happens to the emotional system that an individual cannot integrate, a lot of emotional energy floats around the mind, as well as the physical body. This energy has to go somewhere for the person to continue living. It especially has to leave the mind in order for the person to stay sane. Usually a part of the body volunteers to take it on and so helps keep the whole system balanced and functional. Experience has shown that certain organs have an affinity to certain emotions. For example, the heart has an affinity to love, the lungs to grief, the liver to anger, the kidneys to relationship and so on. In our case, the left kidney took on the emotions. It appears to me that this is already in the setup when the abuse occurs, so the interface will also put a shock pattern around the left kidney (Figure 7.2).

The interface of the mental body that has disconnected in the event also runs an energetic loop (Figure 7.2). The structure that this sets up manifests more over time, rather than immediately, and protects the emotional system. It sets up the warning patterns which we discussed and communicates them to the emotional system. As time passes, these patterns generally grow increasingly rigid and slip out of the conscious mind's control.

This provides a fundamental, though simple picture of the way the body sets up its responses. In reality, the response of the mental and emotional body can be a lot more complex. An event like this can have a lot more far-reaching consequences than I can describe here.

Now that we understand how the body protects itself in case of emotional injury, we can go to the more interesting part—how this can be healed.

Our four-year-old girl has been growing up, and some long-term trouble with the whole urinary tract, especially the left kidney, brings her to the office of a Reconnective Therapy practitioner. The first thing that her body shows in the treatment is that it wants the emotional and the mental body reconnected. The practitioner facilitates this reconnection with the first frequency and the woman goes home.

I use the terms emotional and mental body to facilitate communication. In truth, no such thing as a separate emotional or mental body exists. The energy body and physical body are a unit.

Over the next few days, our client feels tired. She has a strong need to be by herself and just curl up in a place where she feels safe. This gradually disappears and she feels more and more solid and peaceful inside in a way that she never has before. She also notices that she relates differently to her boyfriend. She notices a lot of weird sensations in her kidneys and a pain in them that feels like overexerted muscles.

After about two weeks, she shows up for another treatment. This time many places in the body, and especially the left kidney, want to be connected to the third frequency. This treatment leaves her feeling solid and safe in herself. In another two weeks, the third treatment connects her body in many different places and again, specifically in the left kidney, to the fourth frequency. After this treatment, she has the peculiar feeling for a few days that she is a lot of different personalities that quickly come and go within her psyche, one after another. This feeling is not intense but strong enough for her to notice. In later treatments, the body comes up with other concerns that have nothing to do with the old emotional injury.

Let's see what this looks like on the structural level and how each treatment with the different frequencies affects our client.

The first thing that happened in the treatment was the connection of a part of the interface for the emotional body to the first frequency. Let's say that it was the part that disconnected with the abuse.

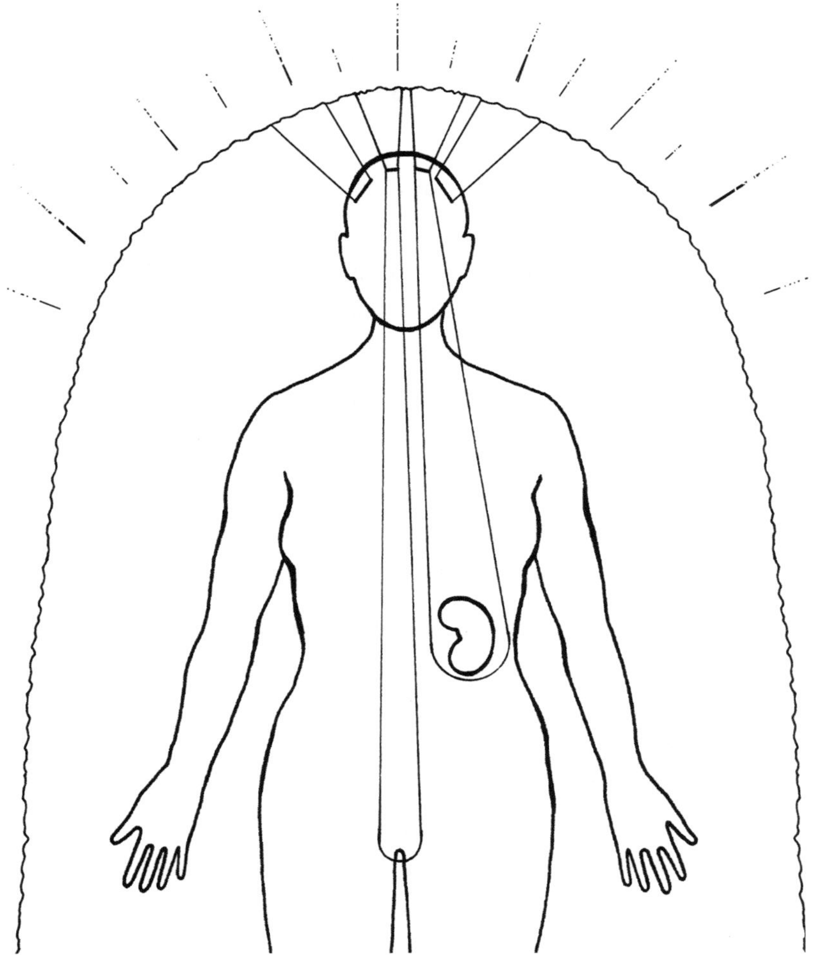

Fig. 7.4. The body after the reconnection of the emotional and mental systems.

A few minutes after the treatment, the emotional shock patterns around the left kidney and genital area stop being generated, so they collapse. Notice that the shock is not released; the body simply ceases to produce it anymore. With this, the kidney and genital area are reconnected automatically to at least the first frequency to a certain degree.

The human emotional and mental systems are usually either not or only partially connected to the first frequency. Therefore, the treatment does not reconnect these systems to their original function, but rather upgrades them to a higher frequency. I could not put this into the drawings because it would have become too complicated.

Along with the reconnection of the emotional system, we have the reconnection of the mental body. As we just learned, the mental system sets up patterns to protect the body from repeating a traumatic event. The protective patterns reflect not only what happened and the nature of the circumstances, but also, to a great degree, personal history. With the reconnection, the mental system stops generating the protective patterns.

The emotional body, the mental body and the physical body do not store the memory of an event—in this case, the rape. They store the way that the person relates to an event. The incident itself is completely neutral.

Once the protective patterns are set, they are self-perpetuating because the function of the mind is to create. Belief systems, whether conscious or not, determine what gets created. In our example, the child believes that intimacy is dangerous. Her fear of intimacy will actually draw dangerous situations connected to intimacy to her as a girl and later as a grown woman. In fact, many adult victims of rape were raped or abused before, usually in childhood. In addition, they often attract abusive relationships and circumstances.

The first frequency is a higher aspect of your self. Here, negative emotions do not exist. Negative emotions are always connected to past experience. Always. If you do a little experiment with yourself and stay totally present just for a moment, you will find nothing but joy.

Once the first frequency is connected into your emotional and mental systems, the way you relate to past experience changes. With this, the way you think and feel about what happened changes, and the related structures of the body heal. This is exactly what happens as a result of dissolving the shock patterns when you reconnect the emotional and mental system with a higher frequency. A treatment like this takes approximately half a minute and can accomplish within two weeks what might otherwise require months or even years of psychotherapy.

A treatment of the emotional and mental body sometimes leaves something like holes in the body. These are places that were previously filled by old patterns that have not yet been filled with something else. This is where the third frequency and frequencies of the higher centers want to connect most of the time. These frequencies are a higher aspect of the people you treat.

In our example, the left kidney has been compressed through the shock pattern for a number of years. Just dissolving the shock pattern might not be enough to restructure the kidney. In the second treatment, the connection of the kidney to the third frequency does the job. This is not just a reconnection of the kidney to its original function, but a connection to a higher frequency.

Let's take this a step further and look at a bigger picture of the whole event. To do this, we'll look into the past-life history of our little girl. About 10,000 years ago, she was in a powerful position where she misused sexual energy. After she died, or towards the end of that lifetime, she could see what she did and how it affected other people. This caused an overwhelming feeling of guilt and the strong belief that she had done something wrong. The feelings were so strong that she could not integrate them at the time and this part of her split off. The feelings of regret were so powerful that they produced a strong imprint in her body that she carried over into her next lifetime.

The human psyche has a deep-seated need to make up for things that we think we did wrong. One of the ways to do this is through self-punishment. Consequently, she decided to experience what she had done to others repeatedly. She lost the memory of the original incident early on, but carried out this structure over thousands of years from lifetime to lifetime. Eventually these experiences accumulated into a gigantic complex of feelings and belief systems and lowered her frequency significantly. I call something like this a causal chain. The rape she experienced in this lifetime was just the last link in a long, causal chain.

Remember that the fourth frequency opens the memory banks for past-life experience and connects a higher aspect of the person into it. This then changes the way we relate to these experiences, which can heal the whole causal chain. We can see that this is the same structure as a treatment of the emotional and mental body. The past is re-interpreted through the connection to a higher aspect of ourself into the interfaces where the original interpretation of the experiences has been set up. The difference between these two treatments is that re-connections of the mental and emotional body are almost exclusively done with first frequency, and this does not have the capacity to open up the memory banks of past-life experience.

Now let's look at the impact of the treatment on our client.

After the first treatment, which was the reconnection of the emotional and mental body to a higher frequency, the little girl that split off after the rape came back in. During the process, the woman experienced a little bit of the needs of the girl for safety and acknowledgement before she integrated.

Many intimate relationships are based on old wounds that fit together like key and lock. Our client, for example, might therefore have attracted somebody into her life who was abusive. Once the little girl is integrated, the adult woman will see this relationship a lot more clearly and probably break it off quickly. After the healing process, she will no longer feel any affinity with her abusive partner. Relationships of this kind are not wrong. They are designed to present great opportunities for healing.

With the connection to the third frequency, our client experiences a higher aspect of herself, which often gives a feeling of solidness.

After the treatment with the fourth frequency, the woman integrates all the split parts from the causal chain (or chains) which were treated. Some of them might just touch the conscious mind for acknowledgement or other reasons before they integrate, which is why she felt many different personalities go through her system. All her relationships based on the old wounds from these times are now going to shift quickly. They will usually either shift to loving ones or fall apart.

It is important to understand that I am using an example to explain a certain structure, nothing more. Disconnections can manifest in our lives with great complexity, but the healing process that I have witnessed many, many times is as simple as I portrayed it here. Other situations might take a few more treatments than we used in this example, but this is basically how I have seen it work numerous times.

The Healing Process of the Mind

With the skill that I now bring to my treatments, more than ninety-nine percent of the people with whom I work do not have to remember any of their old traumas in order to heal. This is possible because the treatments completely bypass the conscious mind, and the higher aspects of the self that are being connected into the body do not hold any kind of dysfunction whatsoever.

Sometimes people drop into the memories and feelings of past experiences during a treatment, but I found a quick and easy way to help them integrate the emotions. First of all, I make sure that the person maintains normal breathing. As long as people breathe, emotions cannot become stuck in their bodies. If people hold their breath, which always happens when they are in fear, the flow of emotional energy in the body becomes blocked.

Second, I make sure that the person stays present. This reminds the body that all the emotions and thoughts that are coming up are from past experience and not from the here and now. If somebody has trouble doing this, I have them look straight into my eyes and nowhere else. So far, keeping the mind in the present and having the emotional energy flow with the breath has always helped. The integration is usually completed within a few minutes.

Chapter Seven

Some of you might ask: "What about talking about what happened?"

I don't think that this is necessary to integrate past experience most of the time. The method that I just provided is the fastest method of integration that I have seen so far.

However, it is vital to discuss something in this context. Some things don't heal unless the client acknowledges them first and consciously allows the process of integration. No rule seems to exist about when this has to happen and when it doesn't. If this conscious acknowledgement is required, we can come to a point in the RCT treatments when RCT can no longer help. I then either work with these people differently, or send them to other practitioners who specialize in what we call "conscious work".

As we already discussed, one of the main jobs of the conscious mind is maintaining the status quo, and consequently, it rejects everything that seems alien. The most alien thing for most people on planet Earth right now is their own essence, or true nature. Therefore, if the conscious mind is exposed to this, it most likely spits it right out and refuses to take it as real. This is a quite a tricky situation. What then can we do to connect to our essence?

One way is meditation. As I understand it, meditation is designed to create an opening in the mind for essence to enter and connect. This happens by allowing it to happen. Basically, you just relax and be with what is. You can also create this opening by giving the conscious mind a problem that it cannot solve without letting go of or transcending its usual patterns.

I know another way and this is love. When two people get together and become one, it opens the door for healing. I have devoted more then twenty years of intense research to finding out how the healing process works and the conditions that allow healing to occur. I have studied many different healing modalities and systems, and I have come to this conclusion: "Wherever two or more are gathered in my name, there I am also." These are Jesus' words, found in The Bible. I have nothing to add.

Love only sees the essence of a person. The rest is nonexistent. When you are in the presence of a loving person, you see and feel more of whom you really are, because their presence reminds you of it. This is fundamentally what we do in RCT. RCT is applied love. The different frequencies are split aspects of love. We can apply them one by one or all at the same time.

Love does not know about separation. That's why you have to drop your boundaries to do a treatment like this. Love does not know about dysfunction and that is why we do not treat it. Dysfunction is a lower-frequency concept. We connect perfection and the mind stops creating dysfunction. This is why we do not have to work to provide RCT. We allow it to happen and it will, because these higher aspects of ourselves are so much closer to whom we really are. This is what RCT is truly about. The rest of the training is about structure and function so that you get to know how to apply it specifically. However, once you are totally loving, you probably no longer need to know about structure and function.

Back to our original challenge: Connecting higher aspects of a person's self that are alien to the conscious mind into the body. We cannot get the information of what and where to connect from the conscious mind, because it does not have it. To receive this information, we need to work with something that knows about it. This is the body consciousness that includes the higher aspects of the person you are treating.

Once we allow the connections, the shift in the subconscious mind or, in other words, the integration of the trauma, takes place within one-to-five minutes. The physical body takes a little while to restructure, about two-to-four weeks, and the conscious mind catches up over time.

A general concept in psychotherapy explains that issues must arise from the subconscious into the conscious mind in order to heal. In our example, if the woman remembers what happened to her, she should heal.

I have not seen this work very reliably and today I think I know why. Though some people have had spectacular healings when they recalled traumatic incidences from their past, others have not. If simply remembering had accomplished the healing, everyone who remembered would have become better.

In my experience, if you work with conscious processing of past experiences, you must take a critical step after you recover the memory, and this is to let go. If you do not let go of your past, it does not heal. Your essence has no space to connect. Theoretically, you can remember your entire history, including all your past lives, and not change. Sometimes letting go is a challenge, because you leave something familiar and do not know what is going to take its place. This is the time of emptiness that you have to experience after you let go. The old is gone, but you have not yet recognized the new. Once you have accomplished these tasks, the healing is complete.

However, at least one more factor is at work: the quality of the therapist. What makes some therapists more effective than others, even when they use the same methods?

In my experience, it is their ability to connect, to drop their boundaries and become one with the person they treat; or, in other words, their ability to love. This completely contradicts Sigmund Freud, who thought that therapists should stay as neutral and disconnected from their clients as possible. He had good reasons for that instruction and his work broke many boundaries in his time. Now, it looks like we are ready to make another step in our evolution.

In my experience, dropping boundaries and becoming one with your client is the only thing that really matters in psychotherapy. This is the condition for healing. The technique used by the therapist is not that important. If the first condition—dissolving boundaries and becoming one—is fulfilled, nothing can stop the healing from happening.

About Dealing with "Negative" Emotions

The idea for this chapter was born from the experiences in the daily practice of RCT therapists. There seems to be a great need to understand emotions, especially those that give us trouble, which we'll call "negative." In truth, negative emotions don't exist. We simply pass judgment on particular feelings that we find unpleasant.

First, we need to understand the nature of emotions. The important aspect here is:

Chapter Seven

<u>We cannot control emotion.</u>

We can learn to control our thinking but not our feelings. An emotion is what it is and we cannot do anything about it. We can suppress an emotion using will power or drugs, but that does not change the emotion; we only numb our capacity to feel it.

Next is something I have already mentioned:

<u>Every so-called negative emotion is a memory from our past.</u>

In the here and now, sadness, anger, frustration and so on do not exist. If we experiment and allow ourselves to be in the present moment even for an instant, we find ourselves happy—not because of anything in particular, simply happy.

Third, we naturally ask:

<u>What should we do when we experience negative emotions?</u>

First, know that the negative emotion is not a problem in itself. The problem is that we do not want to feel it because it is uncomfortable or frightening. Since the negative emotion usually comes from emotional trauma, it triggers a self-protective reaction which wants to make sure that the past event cannot recur. This is important to understand because it explains why we feel the way we do and makes it easier to be patient and gentle with ourselves.

Let me provide a simple example. A person becomes frightened at night. He does not know why but it keeps happening. The body may react too, producing sweating, palpitations and so on. This can go back to an emotional trauma that happened at night, and falling darkness triggers the memory.

Fourth:

<u>It is not important to remember what happened in our past.</u>

Most emotional traumas heal without the recovery of any memory. In the few instances where this might be significant, it tends to come up by itself.

Now, what do you do when you become frightened at night, for instance? Allow yourself to be with the emotion. Do not suppress it and do not identify with it. Walk the narrow path between these two reactions. Stay present with the emotion, but always know that it is merely a memory.

Negative emotions are but a call from a part of yourself from your past that is looking for healing. It talks to you and all it wants is for you to listen. It talks through how it feels. It does not need to be lectured, educated or anything else, just heard. When these feelings come up, drop what you are doing and just feel; be with yourself, with all you feel and think. Do not change anything; just be with it. It generally doesn't take long, maybe a minute or two, before it feels okay and you can go on. In this way, you can help the integration of split aspects.

This process is one of the most valuable skills you can acquire.

It might take time to learn, but once you do, you will be much more yourself, and your life will become much richer in many aspects. It might not always be easy, but it will be greatly rewarding.

About Forgiveness

At this juncture, we must talk about forgiveness, because so many people share a misunderstanding about its nature that has internally enslaved and gagged generations of Christians. Let's begin by asking the following question: What is the source of the impulses that lead people to do certain things and not do others?

To answer, let's construct an example. A man abducts a young child, abuses her sexually and then kills her. What were his motives? What impulses led him to this action and where did they originate? First, we can look at his family history. We find abuse and violence in his upbringing and we could leave it at that. However, this inevitably brings up other questions: Why don't other people, with a similar or even worse history, become rapists and/or murderers? Why do some even become people with an immense capacity to love?

To shed some light on this puzzle, we have to go beyond the obvious family history. Here, we will find agreements that everyone involved in a particular situation made with each other before they incarnated into this life. These agreements were designed to contain learning experiences for everyone who is part of this process: the perpetrator, the victim and anyone else affected. Sometimes the agreement is designed so that a certain event has to happen, while at other times it can be changed or modified through the choices of one or more of those who are part of it.

Imagine that we could draw something like a life map for one of the people involved in the events in our example. This map would contain all the possibilities on his path and all the decisions that he makes along the way. We would see that every decision leads to a particular experience and to further decisions. Amazingly, if we take the last big decision and follow it backwards as far as we can, we end up at this person's pure essence.

If we look more closely at this map, we find decisions that do not seem to have anything to do with the history of an event. They seem to stand completely by themselves. These choices were made completely, or, to a large extent, from essence. This kind of decision has the power to totally turn a situation around and heal long chains of past experiences.

For me, this simply means that I do not know why somebody makes certain choices. It means that a person's history gives me aspects to understand some of the background behind his choice, but that is about it. Essence is involved in every personal decision in a mysterious way that I can neither understand nor explain. Consequently, I begin to see that having the ability to understand and explain some of these connections is not necessarily the most powerful place to be if I want to help somebody and be at peace with what is. This attitude has a depth to it that I cannot describe with words.

What is forgiveness? As I see it, it has nothing to do with judging a person and his actions, while simultaneously telling him that what he has done is okay. Instead, forgiveness has something to do with seeing essence in everything a person does. Whenever you allow this to happen, you cease to experience all judgments and you find yourself at peace with what is. Then you realize that you need forgiveness only as long as you judge others. When you see a person through the eyes of essence, you understand that there is nothing to forgive.

8

The Law of Healing: *Allopathic and Homeopathic Principles*

This subject alone merits a whole book. Indeed, some great German literature from Dr. Herbert Fritsche and others has addressed it at length. In this book, however, I will keep to the basics.

My use of the term "law" here has nothing to do with the way physics understands it. From my perspective, everything that has been created already has its law. In fact, you cannot split a phenomenon and its law; they are a unit. However, they may appear separate to us due to the nature of polarity, in which we perceive and experience natural units in terms of two sides, though in truth, the sides are inseparable. For example, try to breathe in, but never out; find an electric current with a positive but no negative pole. Think of men and women, good and bad and so on.

The law that governs physical matter in the three-dimensional plane is weight or inertia. At the moment matter was created, its law was created with it. Consequently, matter and weight, or inertia, are indivisible; they are a unit.

In my understanding, the law of healing is similarity. Dr. Hahnemann, founder of homeopathic medicine—and Paracelsus, a few hundred years before him—said: "*Similia Similibus curentur*." This is Latin for: "The similar will be cured by the similar." Once the homeopathic principle was formulated, its counterpart had to be created as well, and this is the allopathic principle.

Let's take a closer look into what this means: Homeopathy treats people by applying what is similar to their symptoms. Allopathy treats people by applying what opposes their symptoms. It is nothing more and nothing less than this.

Let me give you a few examples. Everybody knows coffee's impact on a healthy person. He becomes more awake and alert; his senses heighten; he is more emotional and so on. Giving coffee to a tired person who is ready to sleep is an allopathic use of coffee. This means that the symptoms that coffee produces in a healthy person are the opposite of what he is experiencing.

Giving coffee to someone who is hyperactive, over-emotional, over-alert and cannot sleep is a homeopathic use of coffee, because the individual's symptoms are similar to the effects of coffee. In this case, homeopaths call the coffee the "simile" to the client.

You can already see that there is no such thing as a homeopathic remedy. The way it is used determines whether the remedy is homeopathic or allopathic.

When I was a child, my grandma used to make wraps for us when we had high fevers. She would put a cold and wet towel around our calves and then stack a lot of blankets on top of us. Initially, because of the wet and cold towels, we became cold and shivery. To warm up the cold towel, our bodies cranked up their temperatures. At some point, when the towel was warm enough, we became really hot, because we had so many blankets on top of us. Finally, we started sweating.

Look at an average fever. It starts with shivering, moves into increased temperature and finally produces sweat. As you can see, this was a homeopathic fever treatment.

As far as I know, Samuel Hahnemann originated the term homeopathy. He researched and discovered the effects of using substances homeopathically and, along with later homeopaths, tested many of them. Dr. Hahnemann tested them on himself and his family to find out what kind of symptoms—mental and emotional, as well as physical—they generated, and recorded the results meticulously. Over the years, and continuing to the present day, homeopaths have created a gigantic collection of symptoms, the *materia medica*, with thousands of remedies and up to 5000 symptoms per substance.

In his research, Dr. Hahnemann found that if he prepared the remedies in a certain way, they had a more profound impact on his clients and the healing process was easier on them. Hahnemann definitely knew about the existence of the energy body. He also knew that you cannot learn anything about the energy body by analyzing the physical body. He recognized that the homeopathic use of substances initiates a healing impulse that impacts the energy body first, and from there goes into the physical body.

Dr. Hahnemann was a scientist at heart. To study alchemy would have probably been something like blasphemy for him. It didn't help that alchemy had a bad reputation in the early 1800's because of rampant deceit and fraud. Nevertheless, he found his own way to energize his remedies. He developed a process that he called "potencies." This is how it goes:

1. Take one part of a substance—for example, sodium chlorate—and mix it with ninety-nine parts of water.

2. Shake this mixture strongly, let's say 100 times. This is called *Natrium muriaticum* C1. (*Natrium muriaticum* is the old term for sodium chloride.)

3. Take one part of the C1, mix it with ninety-nine parts of water and shake it again 100 times, which gives you Nat-m. C2.

These potencies are commonly used in the C6, C12, C30, C200, C1,000, C10,000, C50,000, C100,000 and so on.

This process is not just about dilution. It is about imprinting the water or any other carrier used, such as lactose or alcohol, with the original substance's information. Some German research shows clearly that these potencies create chemical or other reactions that differ from simple dilutions of the same substance made without the shaking. Equations from theoretical physics provide some understanding for this. They tell us that the shaking lets the electrons of the substances bump against each other and they then exchange information through photons. I think this information is largely stored in the inner dimensions of the electrons (see "The Fourth Frequency" on page 45.) This also leads to the building of clusters in fluids, especially in water, that hold the information about the potencized substance. The dilution makes sure that beyond the C12, none of the original substance remains in the carrier. It is a pure energetic remedy.

Dr. Hahnemann prescribed his remedies according to the principle of similarity. Let's look at a few symptoms of *Bryonia* to see how this works. One of the main features of this remedy is that everything becomes worse from moving. Suppose a client experiences strong stinging pains in his chest from inhalation, which makes his breathing very shallow—a common symptom of pleuritis. Giving him *Bryonia*, for example in a C30 potency, can completely cure this within two-to-three days.

Typical symptoms associated with *Nux vomica* include impatience; poor food choices; outbursts of anger; bad sleep at night, but good sleep in the early morning and constant stress that tends to affect the stomach. This is often called "the manager's syndrome." A dose of *Nux vomica* in the appropriate potency can strongly impact the psyche and the physical body of a person with these symptoms.

According to Hahnemann, this alone is homeopathy. However, this simple knowledge has been watered down and distorted so much that practitioners of the original homeopathy call it "classical homeopathy."

Now I want to look deeper into the homeopathic and allopathic principles. Medical practitioners apply allopathy based on a system of understanding and guidelines that evolved from the paradigms of Western science. I'll briefly outline the fundamental principles of Western science below.

The first principle is the elimination of the subjective. This means that all results have to be gained and interpreted such that the same experiments produce the same results under the same conditons, irrespective of the personality and cultural background of the scientist. In addition, the topic of research must be understandable within the context of logic.

I want to say a few things about the nature of logic. Our minds function in two basic ways. The intellectual part has a distinct structure that is largely independent from the personality. It knows how to connect data through the structure of logic. Logic is not a human invention; it is a mental structure through which we see and interpret the three-dimensional world. Mathematics is the most beautiful expression of this. Because every human mind has this structure, everyone can understand mathematics, regardless of cultural background and personality.

Western science tries to examine exclusively the three-dimensional realm and its laws. This has benefits and drawbacks. One benefit is the clarity of its agreements. This enables scientists all over the world to communicate with each other without having to take cultural and individual differences into account. A downside of this approach is its limited focus. It only studies a few aspects of the existing forces that directly move physical matter. It excludes all other aspects of the forces because they cannot be approached and understood within this paradigm.

Allopathic medicine proceeds according to the paradigm of Western science, with the underlying assumption that all we are is physical matter. It analyzes the physical matter of the body to find out how people become sick and how they heal. Allopathy sees thinking and feeling in terms of body chemistry and nerve impulses, and dysfunction as a chemical imbalance that can be influenced by certain drugs. These drugs are designed to relieve symptoms by either changing the body chemistry or minimizing our experience of them.

Surgery, from my point of view, is not a treatment of disease; it is a simple repair procedure, so I will not discuss it in this context.

Homeopathic medicine recognizes the existence of an energy body that completely rules the physical body. It recognizes that the energy body, or our feeling and thinking, creates the physical body's conditions and not vice versa. As a result, homeopathy tries to heal the physical body by treating the energy body.

I don't know of any way to understand energy by analyzing physical matter and interpreting the results according to the structure of logic. However, we have another aspect of the mind that works quite differently, but is not easy to define. We know it as intuition, clairvoyance and so on. Since I don't quite have a name for it, I'll call it "intuition."

Let me give you an example to show how the intuitive part of the mind works. Imagine you have 1000 jigsaw puzzles of beautiful paintings that you know well, each of which consists of 1000 pieces. Now you have to fulfill the following task. One of these paintings is covered, except for ten puzzle pieces, and you have to guess which painting it is. If you use your intellect, you have to know all the little fragments of all 1000 paintings—a very difficult task, because you need to know the exact location of one million pieces within the 1000 paintings. However, the intuitive part of the mind can see the whole painting within the fragments and know the correct one. We cannot logically explain this knowing; it is just there.

People who have a well-developed ability to use the intuitive part of their mind can accomplish things that are quite astounding. They are only astounding to the intellectual part of the mind though, because it considers these things. Explaining the intuitive part of the mind with words is challenging, but I hope this example gives you a sense of it.

The intellectual mind fragments things by analyzing them. Intuition sees the oneness in everything. I'll now create two hypothetical experiments to examine what the intellectual and the intuitive functions of the mind can accomplish in the discipline of medicine. In these experiments, I want to show that every little impulse, mechanical or energetic, over time can cause a myriad of symptoms in the physical body as well as the mind.

The body's connective tissue is one piece and every tension in the body can be felt everywhere. With this in mind, let's take someone's big toe and pull on it constantly for a period of years with just a few grams of force. Over the years, we research and write down every change that this pull produces. We probably fill a big book with the results, because we find changes in every system of the body and mind.

For our second experiment, let's put an energetic impulse, such as a potencized remedy, into someone's body and write down all the mental, emotional and physical changes that occur over a six-month period. We end up with a book about as big as the one in the first experiment.

Now imagine that you are a practitioner and you have to treat a person with a number of symptoms. With all the complexity of just the physical body, not even considering the mind, how will you determine what is best for the healing? The Western scientific method cannot locate the cause of a disease, because no such thing exists. Every cause has a cause, has a cause, has a cause and so on. You can find **a** cause, but not **the** cause.

If we practice energy medicine, all we have to do is follow the law of healing which, in my understanding, is the homeopathic principle. We do not have to know why someone is sick. Energy medicine works beyond causality. We just follow the law, put it to work in whatever way we want and find the most appropriate treatment. I can find models for how and why Dr. Hahnemann's homeopathy heals people, but I cannot follow the energetic impulse all the way through the body and the mind. When its impact in the physical body unfolds, the results are so complex that I would end up with the above-mentioned tome.

Considering the way the energy body and the physical body interconnect, energy medicine that follows the law of healing seems to me a much more appropriate approach to the phenomenon of disease and healing than the causal one.

Everything that we talked about so far in this chapter raises one big question: What is healing? Is it the disappearance of symptoms, or is there more to it? To shed some light on this, I'll provide a typical, but simplified, sample case from the practice of a classical homeopath.

Every homeopath takes the patient's whole medical history when he or she comes for the first consultation. I have done this many times, and the patterns I've seen are the same most of the time.

In our sample case, the patient is about forty years old and has arthritic symptoms. In the exam, he tells me that as a child he had an ear infection that was treated with antibiotics. The ear improved, but after a while, the infection came back and the same treatment was applied. The situation repeated a few times, and then the ear infections stopped appearing. After some time, the patient had a recurring infection in his tonsils that became chronic; finally, the tonsils had to be removed. In his late twenties, he started to develop arthritis and nothing he did to help it had any lasting effect. After the homeopathic consultation, I gave him just one dose of his remedy and asked him to come back for a follow-up in three months.

In the follow-up, he told me that some time after he took the remedy, he experienced some pain in his throat that stayed just a few hours and then left. Later, interestingly, the old earache came back, stayed for a few days and then vanished. This occurred a few times and then the earache departed for good. Sometime after this, the patient noticed that the symptoms in his joints were starting to become better and better.

Homeopathy's interpretation of these events is that no healing took place from the allopathic treatments he received as a child. They simply pushed the symptoms back into the body. One way to look at this is that every illness has a reason for its existence; it has something to accomplish. Every illness therefore has a certain energetic potential that has to be expressed somehow. With the right kind of treatment, the potential of the disease can be turned into constructive expression. This is a big aspect of what we call healing. Allopathic treatment does not allow the disease to express itself at all, and thus the body continues to bring it up. If the disease is suppressed often enough, the body loses its capacity to create this illness and it manifests as something more chronic. You can see that the disappearance of symptoms does not necessarily mean that healing took place. Within the healing process, the body lets go of toxins that the tissues have stored from suppression of the disease. These are the symptoms that our client experienced.

More than two hundred years of documented experience demonstrates that this interpretation of these patterns has something to it. The success of homeopathy in treating these conditions speaks for itself.

Healing, in my understanding, always raises a person's frequency. It moves people further on their path of evolution, which, on a structural level, raises their frequency. I do not consider any result from any form of medical treatment that does not match these criteria to be a healing.

Chapter Eight

Having practiced classical homeopathy for eight years and RCT for thirteen, I have concluded that healing can only take place when you follow the homeopathic principle, however you do it. Allopathy will never produce any type of healing.

These might seem like absolute statements. Please remember that I do not judge treatment modalities that do not facilitate the healing process as bad. I do not put down the values of allopathic medication. Steroids can save the lives of people; painkillers can make life bearable for those in chronic pain; psycho-pharmaceuticals can help break cycles of anxiety and so on. All I say is that they do not heal anything. We must know what we do in the field of medicine and our clients must know what they expose themselves to. In addition, we should never forget that whatever modality is used, people are delivering it. One friendly word, caring gesture, prayer or anything like them can facilitate a healing process.

Another thing might be important in this context. In an earlier chapter, we talked about how we create our own reality and our beliefs determine what our reality is like. If we believe that we will get the most healing out of a certain procedure or treatment modality, this is where our power is and nothing else may work as well. Choices are the most powerful if they come solely from us. As a practitioner, my job is therefore to relate information to the best of my ability, but not to make choices for others. The more information people have, the better the choices they can make. I try to support people to the best of my ability in their choices about treatment modalities, whatever they are.

Let's see how these principles manifest in energy work.

Like any kind of treatment modality, practitioners can share energy work according to the homeopathic or allopathic principle, depending on their mindset. With energy work, they will very likely find a mixture of both principles, because even if the practitioner's mindset leads him to work according to the allopathic principle, just a moment of oneness with his client will open the door to healing and allow it to happen.

The principle of similarity implies that things are okay the way they are. For healing, we would not apply a remedy or technique similar to something that we think is wrong. This principle of similarity is a mode of complete nonresistance. It understands and honors the oneness of everything. That's why in classical homeopathy we can use the same substance that causes a symptom to heal it. In fact, I will go as far as saying that they are one. If a substance with the ability to cause particular symptoms was not here on the planet, these symptoms would not exist in living beings.

In bodywork, the indirect techniques apply the homeopathic principle. They let the body determine how it wants to move and in which position it wants to be to heal. At their best, they will allow the body to do the healing by itself. The associated movements always go into the lesion. For example, if you treat a muscle that is in spasm, the body will ask you to push the muscle even further together. This seems to be the best position to allow the muscle to relax. The position resembles the way that the lesion manifested. A tense muscle is contracted. If you treat it with an indirect technique, you apply something similar to the tension. You push the muscle even more together: similia similibus curentur. If you treat the muscle with a direct technique, you apply the symptom's opposite. This means that you try to stretch the tense muscle.

In all energy work, no matter what kind, the practitioner is the simile to his client. This means that the more life experience you have as a practitioner, the more aspects of you can be the simile to the person you treat. Until he died on the cross and resurrected, Jesus' life was a perfect example of applied homeopathy. The way he lived made Him the simile to all the people on the planet.

Any type of energy work that manipulates, tries to fix things, exchanges energy and so on works according to the allopathic principle. Often, treatments will involve a mix of the two, because a lot of healing can occur in ways that are beyond the awareness of the practitioner. Spirit will use you for the healing in every moment that you allow it. It does not matter if you are aware of it or not.

RCT is energy work that functions completely according to the homeopathic principle. Resistance, manipulation and judgment have no place in RCT. It simply allows things to happen, catalyzed by two people becoming one.

9

Beyond Causality: *About Grace*

This chapter mostly summarizes certain topics that I covered previously. For those of you who want to become RCT practitioners, understanding this chapter is critical. Let me tell you why.

If you are a healthcare practitioner, your beliefs about the way your treatments work significantly influence their effectiveness, as well as the healing process itself. An example from my time as a classical homeopath will help illustrate this.

I worked as a classical homeopath for about eight years, until I started doing RCT. During this time, I was quite well known for many good and sometimes even spectacular healings. However, I was also feared, because the symptoms of a number of patients became much worse before they improved. This phenomenon became so intense that I decided I had to do something about it. I could no longer accept the idea that people had to suffer before they could heal. I went inside myself to look for an answer and this is what I found.

Dr. Samuel Hahnemann, homeopathy's founder, wrote many books, including the *Organon of Healing Art,* in which he formulated the basic principles of homeopathy. In this book, he said that he had found that healing, especially of a chronic disease, is most profound and lasting when symptoms intensify after administration of a remedy before they become better. For two hundred years, homeopaths have read, believed and experienced this, and their collective experience and belief have created a strong mental field around the planet to which every classical homeopath connected and still connects. This mental field says that the best homeopathic healings involve an initial worsening of symptoms after administration of the remedy.

We already know that the mind is creative, and that what you think—especially what you believe—is what you experience.

I want to make it clear that I honor the achievements of classical homeopathy, past and present. I do not judge it in any way. However, after these insights, I decided to disconnect from this belief. I resolved that my clients were going to heal to the greatest possible degree without their symptoms becoming worse. Now, guess what happened.

My clients experienced the same healings as before, but they no longer suffered through intensified symptoms. Some aggravations still occurred, but to a much lesser degree. This change did not come on gradually; it was instantaneous.

Reconnective Therapy works beyond causality. In RCT, why somebody has something does not matter. How someone's condition relates to his past does not matter. The only thing that matters is allowing the connections to happen.

It does not matter if you find a bacterium, virus, fungus, parasite, accident, emotional trauma, current-life situation, past-life experience, energetic manipulations or whatever, as the cause of a dysfunction. Reconnecting to whatever wants to be reconnected is the only important thing. What happens after this is not your business. The body will take care of itself.

If you look into dysfunction from a causal point of view, you find that no such thing as **the** cause exists. This is simply because every cause has its cause, which has its cause and so on. If you go all the way back, you might end up with a fall out of unity—but what caused this?

If you have a client with pneumonia, you might say that a bacterium caused it. However, you know that if the immune system were fully functional, it would have killed the bacteria before it produced the pneumonia. Therefore, the dysfunctional immune system, not the bacteria, was the primary cause. Now, what caused the immune dysfunction? You can go on and on like this and never discover **the** cause for an illness.

Causality does not help us comprehend the laws and dynamics that govern the interaction of forces and physical matter. Holistic thinking, on the other hand, is connected through parts of the mind that work beyond logic, and it is my experience that you can connect to them any time. You might find new insights arising that are non-rational, immediate and alive. However, you cannot memorize them like a phone number. They belong to the moment. These insights are dynamic and ever changing in relation to individual needs for interconnection and communication.

Sometimes you might discover laws through which energy works and manifests itself on planet Earth. The law of healing, for instance, is homeopathic: similia similibus curentur. Causal analysis could never produce this realization. Homeopathy works beyond causality, but once its energetic impulse manifests in physical matter, it follows causal connections and you can track it through them, because causality is one of the laws of the three-dimensional plane. Remember, the intellectual, linear part of your mind is simply structured this way, and everything that you see through your intellect comes to you through this structure or filter.

Many people in the healing arts believe that past experiences cause dysfunctions. If you take the example from Chapter 7, you see the sexual abuse and the whole causal chain that goes back to other lifetimes. Then, you must ask why the woman started this chain of experience in the first place. Even if you find an answer, you still need to discover the cause for this cause. This whole process does not really go anywhere.

The case study in Chapter 7 clearly shows that as long as this woman does not completely break with her past, she creates the same experience over and over. In other words, her past determines her future. In my experience, knowing your past does not help you break out of it. Only by connecting to more of your essence can you create a different future. It does not matter how this happens; RCT is just one way to facilitate it. It should now be abundantly clear that healing has nothing to do with a person's past. Rather, healing involves a complete break with the past and the creation of a completely different future based on essence.

Looking at this from another perspective, in RCT, healing always goes beyond causality whether the practitioner or client are aware of this or not. You transcend time and space in RCT, and past and future are concepts of linear time and causality. In earlier chapters, I described the higher aspects of yourself that hold no dysfunction whatsoever. These parts, which have never been touched by the fall out of unity, are what RCT reconnects into the body. Here you can see again why RCT only works if you become one with the person you treat for the duration of the treatment.

As a practitioner, you generally get only small insights into the causal chains behind current events, unless you are able to hold a big picture of what is going on with your client. Whatever insights you receive are not, I think, important for the actual healing process. However, sometimes they are important to communicate to your clients. People need to understand as much as possible about what happens to them in a treatment session, because only then can they take responsibility for their body and its healing.

If you see your clients as who they are in their beauty and glory, you will not see any dysfunction, because it does not exist at that level. This is what we connect into the body.

Compassion seems to be the most effective tool for helping clients bridge essence and personality. Compassion connects to a person at the place where he thinks he is. Suddenly, he feels that somebody is there with him. At the same time, it opens the door to essence, his real nature, and so shines a light onto personality that helps merge it with essence.

As far as I currently understand it, this is how RCT works in relation to causality. Comprehending this is essential when you want to become an RCT practitioner.

An RCT treatment always works if you fulfill the conditions laid out in Chapter 6. However, remember that your belief systems might influence the treatment outcome.

Most simply, RCT is about grace as the Bible describes it. Grace does not ask why or how or if. Grace offers healing at any time. It is there at any time and will turn things around for you the moment you allow it. I see this as an aspect of love. Love does not see your past and future, or your dysfunctions and pains. It sees you as who you are and restores your memory of this. From there, your past is reinterpreted and no longer exists as it did previously.

You are not required to grasp and apply all this perfectly when you start offering RCT. If you could, you would no longer be on planet Earth. Nevertheless, connecting to and understanding the basic concept is crucial. From there, you can expand it into more and more aspects of yourself.

10

Dysfunction from the Point of View of Reconnective Therapy

I've already covered many of the topics that I talk about next. However, I feel they are so important that I am going to pull them all together in this chapter.

Talking about RCT in words is extremely tricky. Language, as most of us use it today, is designed to operate within the limits of polarity and address the intellect. Though RCT does not function within the structures of polarity or reason, in this book I must try to communicate about them largely through language. When I teach classes, things are a little easier. There, I always hope that the combination of language, my presence and the things that happen will help people to understand what I am discussing.

Western culture places a strong emphasis on the intellect, or the part of the mind that has the ability to connect empirical facts through the laws of logic. I often find it necessary to convey information in a form that is familiar to the intellect, so that it does not discard it. Then the intellect can serve as a doorway into other aspects of the mind so that the person can see things in different ways. Even if someone has already developed other facets of his mind, it is important to include the intellect and give it the food that it needs to follow what is going on.

I use terms such as "cause" or "dysfunction" that are not really part of RCT. Dysfunction, for instance, does not exist from the point of view of RCT. However, I don't know how to use language to express things differently and still make the book readable. Please excuse this linguistic limitation and be aware of this discrepancy whenever you come across it in these pages.

So-called dysfunction is a creation of the mind that thinks something is wrong. Love sees a person as he or she really is and finds no dysfunction. Whatever we put our attention on grows. Whatever we focus on expands, because we give it energy and thus keep recreating it. If we think something is wrong, then this is what we are likely to experience.

As we already learned, as practitioners, our attitudes impact our clients. In RCT, the healing process is something that we create together with other people by acknowledging their perfection. In this way, we serve as a catalyst to connect this into their bodies. It is not something that we do or give and that another person receives.

I will frequently continue to share using the idiom of Western medicine and its way of thinking and labeling, particularly in Chapter 12. Therefore, remembering what I said in this chapter is imperative. Otherwise, you could get lost and a conflict between reader and author might then become inevitable.

11

The Effectiveness of Reconnective Therapy

Questions about RCT's effectiveness will inevitably come up, especially when you start reading Chapter 12. Therefore, let's address this subject beforehand.

At this stage of RCT practice, I have seen almost every kind of healing imaginable. I have seen the body grow back lost parts, restore dead nerves in the central nervous system, heal acute and chronic conditions in sometimes very short periods of time and so on.

I have seen spectacular things happen in just a few RCT treatments, and I have also seen people take a long time to feel their symptoms shifting. Sometimes conditions did not appear to change much at all. The spectacular healings I have witnessed tell me what is possible, however, they do not mean that it will always turn out this way. Every person has a tendency to heal and a tendency to resist healing. Without the resistance, the individual's frequency would instantly rise so high that he or she would be off the planet and out of polarity.

The resistance is an aspect of personality. (Remember that I define personality as who we think we are.) As we know, in RCT, we do not work with the client's personality. We should honor it, but healing does not come from there.

In RCT, we work with the part of a person that wants to heal. This tendency is an aspect of essence, or who we truly are, and usually is far beyond the conscious mind. Whatever someone does to avoid healing—however deep the wish to die may be—is always an aspect of personality. Essence stays completely untouched by this.

We cannot destroy our essence. We did not create it, thus we cannot uncreate it. Essence is as God made us. Consequently, the tendency to heal is always present. This is what we address and work with when we treat our clients in RCT.

In my thirteen years of RCT practice, everyone who received a treatment had a healing response. I also experienced that once the connections were made, they stayed. So far, I have never had to repeat the same connection twice. This does not mean that it is never necessary to treat the same part of the body more than once. The body only allows a certain amount of restructuring to take place at a given time and then refuses to take any more. After treating a part of the body once, something might still remain to do in other sessions.

The patient's perception of the healing can be a tricky aspect of RCT treatments. My ability to read energies appears to be something rather rare. Usually I can see the restructuring of the mind and body at the moment the healing process begins. I had to learn that just because I can see this does not mean that the patient can feel something changing. Some people feel it right away; some take a few weeks and some can take months, or even a year or more. I have also worked with people who, despite a large number of treatments, never felt any relief from their symptoms.

On a few occasions, I experienced the body simply saying that it did not want treatment. As I understand it, when this happens, a treatment from me or with this modality is not in the person's highest interest for some reason. Sometimes I know why; sometimes I don't. In some cases, I saw that the person had decided to leave the planet, or that they needed the condition to serve somebody else or for other reasons. At times, the body might also have refused treatment because my skill level would not allow me to deal with it effectively.

Now and then, you might feel that the body does not respond when you start a treatment, but it is not completely rejecting the treatment either. This usually indicates the presence of fear. To calm the fear, stay with it and the person in a reassuring way that tells the body that everything is okay and that nothing will happen against its will. You can also try asking a few simple, caring questions, such as: Are you comfortable? Are you warm enough? Anything you need? These can be wonderful door openers, especially with somebody you are seeing for the first time.

Medication of any kind generally does not interfere with the treatment. I have treated people who were on high doses of steroids, painkillers, psycho-pharmaceuticals and so on, and the treatments worked just fine. At some point in the healing process, the body might tell you that the healing cannot progress any further unless the person stops taking a certain medication. This means that the body has healed to such a degree that the medication does not serve it any more. The medication then becomes a limiting factor that prevents the frequency of the body from rising any higher. For women on birth-control pills, this usually happens quickly, sometimes even after the first session.

For a certain period after an RCT treatment, clients should not receive more energy work. In an RCT treatment, the body connects to as much information as it can handle at the moment. Integration time averages about seven-to-fourteen days. During this time, the body usually wants to be left alone in order to complete the changes. Any kind of energetic work you add to this can cause great discomfort, because it might overload the body.

Once the connections are made almost nothing can undo them again. Consequently, whatever you do before or after a treatment is not going to interfere with the treatment itself. The only thing it can do is make the integration either easier or harder on the body.

Groups are the most effective setting for RCT treatments for several reasons. As you remember, RCT works through resonance. Therefore, if you treat somebody in a group for shock release, for example, everyone in the group whose body decides that it can use this treatment connects to this information and gets the same treatment. This means that if someone is sitting in a group of twenty people, he can get as many as twenty treatments. The more the members of a group open up and allow themselves to be at the place of oneness, the more they connect to each other and the more powerful the treatments become. In the introductory classes, where we stay together for five consecutive days, I have seen some phenomenal things happen.

Energy has no boundaries, so you can do this work regardless of the physical distance between the client and you. Long-distance and private sessions have the same healing effect as the group treatments. It might just take more treatments to accomplish the same amount of healing.

One of RCT's most amazing results is the change that occurs in the client's mind. You have already learned how your mind creates your reality, interconnects with your physical body and can be healed. In RCT treatments, every physical symptom that heals includes healing of the related structures of the mind. For instance, the person who heals from hepatitis is not the same as the one who had hepatitis. He is quite different. All the patterns of the mind that created hepatitis have changed along with the elimination of the physical disease. This individual can now start creating a new kind of life and attracting new experiences, because many of the beliefs that came from his interpretation of past experiences changed for him the moment that more of his essence connected.

When I started doing RCT, I was always amazed that so much light radiated from people's eyes after a treatment. Many times, they looked as if they had just had a strong religious experience. I liked it enormously because it was so beautiful, although I could never quite comprehend what the treatment had to do with it. Later on, when I understood that RCT connects more of people's essence into their bodies, I could explain this phenomenon: Some of their pure essence was shining out of their eyes.

Last but not least, if you are skilled and experienced enough, RCT has proven to be very effective in emergencies. I have treated people who have had heart attacks, bleeding into the central nervous system, strokes and acute infections of the central nervous system and other parts of the body. Often the symptoms vanished quickly without any other intervention or repercussions. I did nearly all the emergency treatments long distance.

12

An Extended Understanding of Body Structure and Function

This chapter discusses many of the insights that I have gained while treating people, as well as those gained in other kinds of training. I have been able to validate insights that I received from other teachings through my own experience. I share my personal experience at this time to give you a different way to look at things. I do not claim that what I share here covers everything that might be important to each subject that I address. It is also not my intent to write on every subject, or cover all aspects of a subject according to the standards of Western or energetic medicine.

The areas about which I have chosen to write in this chapter share a common thread. Though most symptoms people develop have their own individual history, a number of things you will find in your clients follow the same basic structure most of the time. These constitute part of my subject matter.

All the subjects I have chosen to write about have another thing in common. They contain information that, to my experience, is not widely known within the health care and healing community. I feel that it might be important for you to have this knowledge, as it can facilitate healing in your clients. It also gives you an extended understanding of the structure and function of the physical body and its interconnection with the energy body.

At all times, please, remember that RCT works beyond causality and does not treat dysfunction. I use the words "cause" or "dysfunction" to describe certain conditions only because I must in order to communicate and write comprehensibley.

To get a clear picture of what I offer in this chapter, first read the sections, "Connective Tissue and Tension" through "Biomechanics", pages 155-171. They provide information that applies to many of the other chapter sections.

In this chapter, the term "body" refers exclusively to the physical body.

Connective Tissue and Tension

The connective tissue of the body is one piece. This means that every little contraction or movement of one part of the connective tissue affects every other part, wherever it is. I first learned this in craniosacral therapy classes at the Upledger Institute in Germany. Their teachings about connective tissue completely confirmed my experiences in my own practice.

Let me give you an illustration of how this manifests in the body. If you pull on the little toe of your right foot, the pull travels all the way up your leg, through the sheaths of the peripheral nerves into the *dura mater* and finally ends up in the sphenoid bone of the skull. The position and mobility of this bone gives you the sum of all the tension in the connective tissue of the body.

In one of the classes, we conducted an experiment. One practitioner held the sphenoid bone, while another one treated. With every release in the body, the sphenoid bone changed its position. This also works the other way around. Tension in the *dura mater* can be felt throughout the whole body and shows very clearly the pull that the *dura* exerts on these parts of the body, the direction as well as the magnitude.

In my experience, this goes a lot further. Every tension in the body also travels via the nerves into the brain and vice-versa. This means that it literally pulls on the brain, or tension in the brain can be felt in related parts of the body. I discuss this in detail when I talk about the central nervous system (CNS). With every release of physiological tension, the brain structure shifts. Treatments with RCT can be powerful, and consequently the brain structure can shift a lot. Since our day-to-day perception is adjusted to a certain tension in the brain, after a session I recommend to my clients that they drive extra carefully for a few days, until their perception has readjusted.

I find that you can track any tension in the body everywhere throughout the body. Our pull on the toe can be felt in every organ and muscle, in the brain and bones, in the biomechanics of the body—simply everywhere. This means that after a treatment in which tension is released, the whole body shifts. Every part of the body finds a new position that is less tense and more mobile than before. Many specific and typical things accompany tension in certain areas. I talk about this in the related sections of this chapter.

Body Protection

In Chapter 6, I gave an example of how the body protects itself. I talked about the shock pattern that the body creates to keep the energy of a physical impact from traveling into the brain. The body also protects itself in other ways.

In this book, I use the term "shock" to describe an energetic phenomenon. It has nothing to do with shock as Western medicine understands it, where the blood vessels dilate, blood drains out of the brain into the feet, and paleness, fainting or even death can result.

Let us start with a description of the different shock patterns. You already know about the physical shock pattern, but this is not the only kind. Shock can be triggered by exposure to radioactivity, toxicity, electrocution and sepsis. The resultant shock patterns, including the ones in the central nervous system, are set up through different energetic interfaces than the physical shock patterns. In electrocution and physical impact, the body has to deal with energies, while with toxins and sepsis, the body actually has to deal with substances. In the case of exposure to radioactivity it might actually be both.

All shock patterns serve the same purpose: They keep a damaging impact enclosed in the area where it hit and prevent it from distributing all over the body. This is accomplished through a sphere-like energy field that encapsulates the energy of the impact as we discussed in detail in Chapter 6. In a septic shock it works a little differently, but this is such a rare phenomenon that I will not discuss it here. Tissue compression is another effect of a shock pattern on the physical level. This effect is of great importance for several reasons.

Imagine the following: You are a practitioner of RCT and you are treating somebody who received a strong hit in the rib cage just a few hours ago. You know and can see that a physical shock pattern has formed, but the body does not ask you to help release it. This can happen for two reasons. First, there is a delay between the moment when the damaging incident occurs and the point at which the body opens up to receive RCT treatment. This can be anything from a few minutes to two days. I do not know why. Commonly after surgery, for example the body opens for treatment forty-eight hours after the intervention. The second reason might be that the patient is bleeding internally and his body needs the shock pattern to remain there to compress the tissues and limit the amount of blood coming out of the injured tissue. If necessary, this compression from a shock pattern can become extremely strong. People who work in emergency rooms know that the spleen can start bleeding up to two days after it is injured. Internal injury of the spleen is life threatening and the body consciousness knows this. It will therefore set up an extraordinarily strong shock pattern that compresses the tissues of the spleen enough to prevent the blood from escaping. I don't know why, but sometimes it cannot maintain the strength of the shock pattern long enough to give the spleen time to close the wound and it starts bleeding again.

When the body has to deal with toxic substances, it protects itself differently than it does with energetic impacts. The basic goal of the protection stays the same: Keep the foreign substances localized in the place where they came in contact with the body, and prevent them from spreading potentially causing more damage or even death.

Substances are energy as well as physical matter. Thus a shock pattern keeps the information that it carries confined to an area as small as possible. Then, through the compression of tissues, it makes it more difficult, if not impossible, for the substances to be absorbed by the tissues and subsequently moved into the blood stream or lymphatic system. Finally, it changes the permeability of cell membranes in the area of the contact and prevents the toxins from getting into cells or through cell walls into other parts of the body.

As I explained in Chapter 6, the way most of our bodies are structured right now, shock patterns remain in the body for a lifetime if untreated. I have been trying to find out why and have come up with the following explanation. A shock pattern is a time-space capsule. The impact—and with this, the event as it happened—is frozen into it. Once an accident is over and the main healing is done, the body might say,

"OK. Now let's dissolve the shock pattern." and opens it up. However, the event is held in the pattern as if it is happening right now. As a result, the self-protecting mechanism is triggered again and resets the same shock pattern. After this, I don't think that the body tries to resolve a shock pattern again by itself. I do think that as the body raises its frequency, at some point it will be able to resolve its own shock patterns. For example, I have seen a man who was able to raise his frequency through the practice of advanced *chi gong* and *tai chi*, so that he was able to let the body dissolve shock patterns by itself.

Sometimes the body creates an accident because it needs the shock pattern to lock emotional energy into a certain part of the body. This can occur when the emotional storage capacity of this part of the body is exhausted, but it still has to keep it in there for various reasons.

Let me give you an example of the impact and treatment of a radioactive shock pattern. A woman in her early fifties came in because she had not been able to turn her head for the past twenty-seven years. All I found when I looked at her was the thymus gland, and I communicated this to my client. At this time I did not have a lot of experience and I was wondering how the thymus gland could contribute to a stiff neck. She told me that she had undergone radiation treatment as a little baby, when the doctors tried to shrink what they considered an enlarged thymus gland. I helped the body to get rid of the shock from the radiation in her thymus gland and connected the thymus gland to the second frequency information about structure and function. When I saw her for another treatment a few months later, she had good neck mobility. The shock in the thymus gland, and with this the compression and adhesion of the tissues, had been so strong that it had tightened the whole chest and neck area and so caused the stiff neck.

If you do not have some experience as an energy-medicine practitioner, shock patterns can be hard to perceive, because they encapsulate a part of the body and can be quite dense. If you try to read the energy body and you look at a shock pattern, you might not see anything. If you have your hand on a part of the body and you ask it what it looks like, all you might get is something that seems like thick fog. If you have enough experience, you might be able to interpret this as a shock pattern, but I tell you they can be easy to miss.

Shock patterns are one of the major ways that the body protects itself. However, it has many others, and inflammation is another important one. Let me explain this to you.

All the cells, parts and functional units of the body are in permanent communication with each other. They constantly exchange information. If an area of the body was dysfunctional and could not fix itself, it would try to exchange information about its dysfunction with other parts of the body. Information about this dysfunction would spread through the body and imprint in other cells. The body does not want this to happen and it uses a simple method to prevent it. It allows an inflammation to take place in the dysfunctional area. Once the inflammation is present, the immune system steps in and puts this area under quarantine until the problem is fixed. This means that the immune system shuts the area down and does not allow any communication with other parts of the body. This is exactly what the body wants, and so it does not allow the inflammation to heal. It maintains the status of inflammation to a certain degree, to keep the immune system activated and the area closed down.

This causes compression in the tissues, glues them together and results in limited communication within the body as well as between the affected body part and the energy body. It also constantly consumes a certain amount of immune system capacity so that it cannot be used for other purposes.

Almost everyone I have seen for treatment has a significant amount of this type of inflammation in the body. Typically, they are tiny pockets, but the body can have a lot of them. They are significant in the spinal cord in cases of multiple sclerosis (MS) or in areas of old injury. With most healings I see, much of this type of inflammation leaves the body, simply because the body no longer needs it.

Muscles that tighten to protect an area of diminished mobility provide another form of body protection. I call this protective muscle spasm, as did DCR (Dialogs in Contemporary Rehabilitation), who first taught me about this.

Let's again use the client with radioactive shock as an example. When the radioactivity hit the thymus gland and the surrounding tissue, this area went into shock, as we discussed above. On the physical level, the affected tissues contracted, went into spasm and stayed there. This had two major consequences.

First, because the connective tissue is one piece, the contraction of the thymus gland, as well as the surrounding tissues, pulled on all the tissues of the body. However, the pull was strongest on the tissues that were next to the area in shock.

Second, the exposure to radioactivity damaged tissue in the area around the thymus gland. Along with this, protective inflammation appeared in the area. This not only compressed the tissues through the shock pattern, but also glued them together, mostly due to the inflammation.

When you move your body, especially when you stretch, all the tissues involved move. You have many strata of tissue layered upon each other, and they all move in different directions and change lengths when the body moves. To do this, they have to be able to glide over each other. In an area of damage, like the one here around the thymus gland, the tissues are contracted and glued together and therefore not able to glide. If the client makes a move that tugs on these tissues, they can tear apart and be damaged if the pull is strong enough. The body consciousness knows this. To avert this possibility, it tightens all the muscles necessary to prevent movements that can harm the affected tissue. In the case before us, the main muscles involved are the major and minor pectorals, the scalenes and the sternocleidomastoid. The pectoral muscles compress the thorax and the scalene anterior, medius and posterior pull up the rib cage and pull down the transverse processes of the second-through-the-seventh cervical vertebrae. This compresses the cervical spine and reduces its mobility. Finally, every turn of the head pulls on the thymus-gland area, so the body tightens the muscles that turn the head, i.e., the sternocleidomastoid. This phenomenon is what I call protective muscle spasm.

Clearly, what gave our person trouble in the first place was not the radiation burn, but the protective muscle spasm that safeguarded the burn area and compressed the cervical spine and the thorax. This is the complex that did not allow her to turn her head.

I have almost never seen a muscle that is chronically in spasm that was not protecting something. The only exceptions are cases in which the muscle is directly hurt in an accident or becomes overexerted.

Most of the time, it does not make any sense to work on tight muscles directly. If you want the muscle to relax, find what it is protecting. Help heal this and the protective muscle spasm will go. Muscles can protect physical body structure as well as emotions that are locked in the body.

Shock patterns, protective inflammation and protective muscle spasms are the body's main self-protective mechanisms about which I know. I already discussed the ways that the mind protects itself in Chapter 7.

Compensation

I use the term "compensation" to refer to the body's ability to deal with dysfunction in the least damaging way. To me, the body's methods for compensation are absolutely stunning and unique to each individual. I'll provide just a few examples, and talk about some common patterns to give you some sense of what can take place.

Let's start with simple biomechanics. When someone breaks a leg, the body responds quite simply: It does not allow the individual to put weight on the injured limb. He must put all his body weight on his other leg. The body gets him to do this through pain. The healthy leg compensates for the injured one.

If we look at the same person ten years later, we see that his break did not heal completely; the affected bone is still a little unstable and not as strong as the other one. As we know, the body consciousness is aware of the complete status of everything that goes on within it at any given time. Therefore, it certainly knows about this. This person now walks down a hill, bends his foot a little as he steps onto a rock and all of a sudden finds himself on his butt.

The leg gave out. It had to do this. The strain on the injured bone would have been too much, so the muscles did not hold up the leg. After all these years, his body still favored the healthy leg. The body shifted everything around to get into the optimal position to balance the unstable bone in the damaged leg. This compensation affected all the muscles—the biomechanics of the pelvis, the spine, the positions of the bones in the skull, the organs, the spinal cord, the brain—just about everything in the body.

This situation demonstrates one of the major reasons why our method of diagnosis is so successful. We communicate directly with the body consciousness to find out what it wants to have treated, rather than trying to find our way through all the compensations of the body to determine what to treat.

Now we go from biomechanics to energetics. Hahnemann's two-hundred-year-old book, *Organon of the Healing Art*, tells us that if you suppress a skin condition, you might end up with something a lot worse. He knew about the energy body and its governance of the physical body and he called it the "dynamis".

Every dysfunction has a certain energetic potential. For example, imagine a person with chronic grief he cannot integrate. Unintegrated emotions exist as energy that floats around in the system and has to go somewhere. Most importantly, it has to go out of the mind. Usually, a part of the body volunteers to take it on to keep the whole system stable. In our example, the lung says that it will take on the grief, and so the emotion goes into the lung and manifests there as a chronic, low-grade infection. Now the body says that this is not really necessary. Let's take this energy and manifest it as a skin rash, because it causes much less damage there than in the lung. Believe me, I have never treated a skin condition that has not been pushed out there by the body to get it out of an organ or the nervous system. The skin's exposure to toxicity is the only exception.

Suppressing disease symptoms that have a high energetic potential can be extremely dangerous. The body is already in trouble. It has to manifest these energies quickly and in a way that allows it to stay alive. If you interfere with this and suppress the symptoms, this energy has to manifest as something else really fast. The consequences for your client can be disastrous, involving anything from life-threatening conditions to insanity to death. In my experience, any kind of disease or symptom can have a high-energy potential, whether it manifests primarily physically, emotionally or mentally.

Biomechanics

This chapter does not reveal anything new. Everyone who has studied a little bit of hands-on therapy has learned about biomechanics. A thorough grasp of the basics of biomechanics is important for understanding the content of some of the sections that follow. I'll therefore go through some basics, and talk about the pelvis, spine, skull, teeth and organs.

The dura mater is fixed at S2 (the second bone of the sacrum), the foramen magnum and the bones of the skull. Consequently, every pull on the dura also pulls on all these parts and on the brain.

Remember everything in the body is connected through the connective tissue. As long as the sacrum is in the right position and mobile, nothing pulls on the dura and the body has no tension. I have not yet seen this ideal structure in anyone.

The sacrum plays a key role in biomechanical balance. The spine and the skull sit on it, and both ilia are connected to it through the sacroiliac joints. The sacrum consists of five bones. These bones are not fused. They are supposed to be mobile in relation to each other. They can get out of alignment, which can cause a significant amount of discomfort. I have seen this mostly in people who have been bedridden for a longer time.

Mobility of the sacroiliac joints is also important to biomechanical balance. If these joints are not mobile, every leg movement causes the sacrum to move in an unnatural way.

Another important factor is also at work here. About fifteen percent of the population has one or two extra joints between the ilium and the sacrum. The extra joint(s) sits right underneath (towards the front of the body) the posterior spina iliaca superior (psis). It is a real joint, with a capsule, ligaments and everything else a joint requires. If these joints are stuck, you cannot mobilize a person's pelvis, no matter what you do.

If a vertebra is out of alignment, it pulls on the pelvis as well as the skull and vice-versa. In between the vertebrae are discs. They consist of a shell made out of fibrous material and a gel-like core. As people walk around all day, the weight of the body presses on the discs and pushes more and more water out of them. During the night, when they lie down, pressure on the discs is minimal and so they pull in water again and expand. As a result, people can be more than an inch taller in the morning than in the evening.

If certain discs are under constant pressure due to protective muscle spasm or due to any other reason, these discs do not expand as much at night as those without pressure. However, during the day, they have to take the weight of the body again. Consequently, over time, they shrink more and more, until the day comes when uncomfortable symptoms arise. This generally produces a visit to the doctor and an x-ray. The pictures will reveal one or more flattened discs. The medical profession generally considers these flattened discs to be used up and believes that nothing can make them expand again. However, I have seen many discs re-expand when the chronic compression is removed. I have seen this work to sometimes amazing degrees.

Next I want to describe the interconnection between the teeth and the body, especially the CNS. With all that we have discussed, it should be clear that every tension in the body affects the bite. Once the body has adjusted the bite to a certain tension, releasing this tension changes the bite and the body has to readjust it.

Teeth are highly elastic structures, built in an amazing way to do their job of chewing. Teeth have bone material inside, which is elastic but too soft to be confronted with hard materials that need chewing.

The outside is a thin layer of crystalline calcium that has fluoride atoms in its grids. Its hardness is M-O-H-S 9, which makes it, together with corundum, the second hardest natural substance on the planet. This keeps the teeth extremely hard, without sacrificing elasticity. It makes sure that they don't wear down too easily or crack when you unexpectedly bite on something solid, such as a cherry pit.

Teeth and the bite change to adjust to changes in body tension. The body then grinds them down to adjust the bite. My craniosacral therapy teachers in Germany proved that the bite changes with every little shift in body tension. They demonstrated this to a group of dentists. One instructor decompressed the temporomandibular joint (TMJ) on a dentist whose bite had been perfectly adjusted just before that. After the treatment, the bite was off. It was adjusted again. Then they did another TMJ decompression and the bite was off again.

Certain ceramic materials used for crowns appear to be too hard and inelastic to allow the body to adjust the teeth to different tensions. Tension then builds up elsewhere to compensate. The body also seems to have a hard time grinding down ceramic crowns to create the necessary adjustments to the bite. Tension that builds up in teeth can cause a lot of pain, not necessarily in the teeth, but anywhere in the body.

One example from my practice clearly shows the interconnection between the teeth and the CNS. A client had been in an accident years ago, in which she broke a number of bones and injured parts of her CNS. She had a few treatments with me and continued to work with a D.O. in town who was trained in RCT. They also networked with a dentist to get her bite fixed. The osteopath would treat her to release the tension in her CNS and then the dentist would adjust her bite to work with the changes from the release. Things seemed to be going just fine, when one day she called me. She had terrible pain in her lumbar spine that came up after another bite adjustment. I treated her right away and mobilized some nerves in the spinal cord. This took care of the pain immediately. From what I could see, the body had pushed the spinal tension into the bones of the jaws and the teeth because the body considered it to be less troublesome there. This tension changed her bite. Then the dentist did a little bit too much of an adjustment on the bite and this pushed the tension right back into the spinal cord and caused the pain. This connection is quite common and I have seen it a number of times.

The biomechanics of the body never go out of alignment unless a force is involved. This is the most important thing to remember. For example, if you find the left ilium (pelvic bone) is too high and internally rotated around a horizontal axis, a pull through the connective tissue is moving it into this position and holding it there. As long as this pull is present, it makes no sense to readjust the ilium, because it will be hauled out of place again. You might find that the body wants you to treat the left lung. A week after the lung treatment, the body might show you the left ilium for readjustment. This means that the pull on the left ilium has eased to a certain degree, but the body needs some help to get it back into the right position.

There is one exception to this rule. If the body has been subjected to a sudden physical impact, the biomechanics can be pushed out of alignment. If the impact was strong enough, the body might not be able to reestablish alignment by itself. With accidents, a lot of different factors come into play, as we will see later.

With RCT, you can adjust any part of the body's biomechanics by simply connecting this part of the body to the information about its correct position and it will move there by itself, usually within a few minutes. You don't have to know how these parts are out, around which axis they are rotated or if they are up- or down-slipped. When I demonstrate this procedure to professionals like chiropractors or osteopaths, they are always stunned to see that it really works like this.

If you have now understood the fundamentals of RCT, you know that you cannot go in and adjust the biomechanics just because you can see that they are out of alignment. The body consciousness knows what has to happen first and communicates this to you. It also lets you know when it makes sense to readjust the biomechanics.

If you adjust one part of the biomechanics, all the others automatically follow, because they are all interconnected. For instance, an adjustment of the sacrum or the ilium can loosen up all the vertebrae and the bones of the skull and vice versa. The body tells you what will be most effective to treat at any given time. Once you can follow this process, you might be amazed at how much can be accomplished in one treatment.

The body's main goal in a treatment seems to be mobility, not biomechanical alignment. I once treated a man in his early sixties whose lungs had spontaneously collapsed when he was in his twenties. Since then, both lungs have been strongly in shock, and with this, highly compressed. Both lungs pulled forcefully on both of the ilia and moved them cranially, which means towards the head. When I checked on the biomechanics of the man's pelvis, both ilia were perfectly aligned but completely immobile.

His body asked me to treat one of the lungs, and within a few minutes, the ilium on the same side as this lung dropped down significantly. Now, his pelvis was no longer aligned, but was a lot more mobile. The treatment of the other lung followed a week later and that brought the other ilium down.

I have observed that with the release of tension that occurs after treatments, the biomechanics of the body can go in all directions. One time you might find them perfectly aligned and another time completely off. However, their mobility will gradually improve with every treatment. This phenomenon usually shows up most strongly in the first treatments. After a series of treatments, usually the body's biomechanics become more and more aligned and stay there.

Because all parts of the body are interconnected, I could easily get lost in describing what can happen with all kinds of tension. Instead, I am keeping to the basics here. The more you understand the oneness of all parts of the body and their interconnections, the easier it will be for you to access and understand what you need to know. This book can give you some information with which to start. Once you become more experienced, you will be able to follow any kind of tension through the body and get the information you need. This skill will allow you to attend to the individual needs of your clients, which will be different with every treatment you do.

Accidents

In Chapter 7, you saw that nothing happens to you out of the blue. Accidents are something that you create, usually unconsciously. Knowing this, you can understand that accidents serve a purpose.

Only the part of an injury that has already served its purpose and is no longer needed heals. In RCT your higher aspects connect to the body. Everything might then shift in such a way that the accident no longer serves a purpose. This is not up to the judgment of the practitioner. As always, the body shows you.

I have seen a lot of accidents that served to loosen up certain complexes and fixations in the mind, as well as in the related parts of the body. It is as if the accident blew a hole in the wall of the immobile body as well as its mental and emotional structures and opened all this up for healing to come in. I have done treatments on people with recent injuries that also facilitated the healing of much more than the recent injury. Every accident seems to have an emotional component, and this can show up in the treatment as well.

It often happens that an accident, especially a minor one, occurs to expose older accidents that have not been completely healed. I have had a number of clients who came in with a minor injury that required just one or two treatments. However, the pain did not subside or became even worse. Usually, this happened when the damage from an old injury was exposed by the most recent injury, and came up from the tissues to get attention.

Some people are accident-prone. I've observed that they either injure the same parts of their body repeatedly, or they always have the same kind of injury. For instance, some people always burn or cut themselves. If I look at the whole process through the structure of linear time, I find that this goes back to past-life experiences that have been stored in the body. The body generally wants the treatment to take care of the actual injuries or their leftovers first, and then it goes for the integration of the past-life experience. The treatments can change the pattern of injuries and they stop happening or at least occur less frequently.

Stronger injuries that leave a condition that lasts for a lifetime, such as a spinal cord injury, are choices. These choices, when and however they were made and for whatever purpose, need to be honored. With RCT, we have the capacity to facilitate spectacular healings, even for injuries to the CNS. Once your skill is up to this level, your integrity and level of understanding should be there as well. This means that you understand that you are dealing with something really big.

An injury like this reflects an identification before it actually happens. For instance, a person who sits in a wheelchair identifies with this condition long before he or she gets there.

Disability is a relative concept. Imagine staying in a community of people where mind-to-mind communication and teleportation are common. Our ability to participate in the life of that community would be limited. If we lived there, special arrangements would have to be made for us. Similarly, if everybody sat in a wheelchair, we would not think of this as a disability.

Letting go of a backache is usually not a big deal, because the identification is not all that strong; i.e., it is not difficult to let go of the related structure in the mind. The more that we identify with something, the harder it is to let go of it. If we think that we are our injuries, what is left of us after they have healed? Healing is always more or less a leap of faith, because it leads into the unknown, especially since most of us have lost the memory of who we really are. We don't necessarily feel small leaps. Bigger ones can take a while. Sometimes we feel as if we're jumping off a cliff into deep water, knowing that we can't swim, yet trusting that somehow we'll know how before we hit the water. The more often we do this in life, the more we know that we are taken care of, and that we never fall any deeper than into the hands of God.

People who come in with serious conditions give their lives into our hands. They need to have the feeling that we, as practitioners, can fight death and the devil, and that everything is going to be fine. In my opinion, this is what it takes to be a good practitioner. We don't have to talk about it. Our clients feel it and this helps them allow things to happen that go far beyond what they dream is possible—until they remember that they can fight death and devil by themselves.

Whiplash

To begin our look at accidents, I want to start with something on the physical level that is easily understood through biomechanics. If you sit in your car and you get rear-ended, your head is thrown backwards because of the inertia. This means that the spine goes into extension and the sacrum is pushed downwards. The same movement jams the first cervical vertebra (C1) into the occipital condyles. Then the head jerks forward and the spine goes into flexion. With this, the sacrum is pulled upwards. With these sudden movements, the sacrum usually gets stuck either in the upper or lower part between the ilia, and C1 gets stuck between the occipital condyles. In every whiplash injury I have seen that caused symptoms, C1 has been stuck between the occipital condyles, and the sacrum has been stuck between the ilia.

The sacrum is the lowermost part of the spine as C1 is the uppermost. In this situation, then, both ends of the spine are immobilized. This greatly limits spinal movement.

When C1 is jammed into the occipital condyles and stuck there, this joint can be injured if it breaks loose through sudden movements. The body now has to protect the area from these movements and, as we know, does so through tightening the appropriate muscles. In addition, nerves and blood vessels can be compromised. All of these factors cause stiffness and pain in the neck.

If the impact is very strong, the neurons in the spine and even in the brainstem can sustain damage through the sudden flexion of the spine and the resulting strain on the nerves of the spinal cord. The flexion can also cause a sudden strain in the blood vessels in the neck, especially the spinal artery. The extension of the spine can cause a strain, especially in the vertebral artery. This sets up a shock pattern in the spinal cord as well as the blood vessels and generates a powerful protective reaction by the body.

When the sacrum is stuck between the ilia, there is usually no danger of injury through the wrong movement. As a result, this position does not cause a strong protective reaction in the body. This means that most of the time people will not feel any pain in this area after a whiplash injury.

Readjusting the sacrum is generally all it takes to heal a whiplash injury without an associated shock pattern. Once you know how to do this with RCT, it takes about thirty to sixty seconds! This usually mobilizes C1 as well. If the client experienced a slightly stronger impact, you might have to give the body some help to mobilize C1.

To readjust the sacrum, you simply have to connect it to the information that tells it where it has to be in the body, and it will move there by itself within a few minutes. You do not have to know anything about the sacrum's misalignment or position, around which axis it is rotated or if it is ascended or descended. Just listen to what wants to be reconnected and how the body wants to do this.

Powerful impacts might produce a shock pattern in the neck tissues. Then the body might ask to have this released before you treat the sacrum. If the impact injured the blood vessels and/or the CNS, you might have to release these shocks first and restructure these areas before you can get to the sacrum and C1.

Remember that in RCT the body always tells you what to do. Never just go ahead and work on the sacrum, because you know that your patient had a whiplash injury.

Concussion

I use the term "concussion" in a broader way than Western medicine does. This discipline uses it to describe the complex of symptoms that can show up in someone after he has hit his head quite hard. These symptoms include headache, nausea, lack of focus, dizziness, a general feeling of being out of it and so on.

As I see it, when someone hits his head hard, the physical body and the energy body go out of alignment. The energy body looks like it is vibrating around the physical body. The energy body around the head looks as if it is pulsating, with the center of this pulsation sitting in the middle of the head. This phenomenon not only occurs in the head, but I have also seen it in the shoulders and the pelvis, when they are hit hard and suddenly.

An energetic interface in the brain sets up the concussion pattern. I am not quite sure why the body does this, but it appears to keep the energy of the impact out of the brain. I do not understand at all why the body also does this in other places.

Concussion patterns can stay in the body for a number of years. Usually the immediate symptoms go away after a while but something remains—compression of tissue and non-synchronicity between the energy body and the physical body. This seems to cause a certain amount of distress and a wide variety of symptoms that can vary from person to person.

Through the reconnection of the interfaces, the energy body and the physical body usually realign within a few minutes after the treatment. Sometimes the client feels a huge sense of relief, a calming of the whole system. Many symptoms can vanish that you would never have connected with a concussion. If the client has one, or even more than one concussion pattern in his body, this usually shows up for treatment first, before the body shows other parts to treat.

Bone Injuries

I am aware of three different degrees of bone injury. The first is the plain break. Pain and dislocation make this degree easily detectable, and it usually shows up pretty clearly in an x-ray. It needs surgical attention. The bones need to be put back together in the right position and fixed there, by whatever method. Then, with RCT, the shock release and the bone restructuring can take place. By restructuring, I mean the bone connecting to the information about its perfect structure and function. This has proven to reduce the healing time tremendously.

In my practice, I often see breaks that have not healed completely. The bone cells have not connected strongly enough, or an area of the break got left out in the healing process. Frequently, this cannot be detected in an x-ray and does not cause any symptoms in the affected area.

This can happen for a number of reasons. Old unintegrated emotions may be tied into the bone structure. I once treated a marathon runner who had broken a leg years earlier and experienced pain since then. I gave him one treatment for emotional integration and a few days later his leg felt better then it had since the accident.

Some kind of energy blocks may be present (see "Strange Energy" on page 230), or, as we discussed earlier, the condition may serve a purpose. Sometimes the shock and the emotional trauma from the accident were so great that the body could not complete the healing. Many more reasons exist, but they vary greatly from person to person.

Inappropriate comments from physicians during surgery can also generate emotional trauma that gets stuck in the bones. Every surgeon needs to know that when people are unconscious from the anesthetic during surgery, they hear everything spoken in the room. Most of them do not consciously remember what they heard after they wake up, but nevertheless, it impacts their emotions. I have treated a number of people with emotional shocks induced through the disrespectful use of language during a surgery. These shocks prevented the completion of the healing process.

Let's use a break in the right femur to illustrate the consequences of incomplete healing. Let's say the healing moved forward to the point where the symptoms disappeared and the x-ray looked clear, even though the break was not fully healed. The right femur thus remains less stable than the left one and the body knows this. First, the body will prevent any kind of movement from happening that might put the bone in danger of breaking again. Second, it will take as much of the workload as necessary from the right leg and put it on the left one. As you already know, the body does this by tightening the respective muscles. This process of compensation is too complex to describe here. It is also different for each individual.

In order to see the potential implications of this condition, let's assume that the client in our example has a strong protective spasm of the right psoas muscle. Among other things, this compresses the right sacro-iliac joint (sij) and all the discs on the right side, from L1 through L5 (the space between first lumbar vertebra to first sacral bone, also used for first through fifth lumbar vertebrae), because of its pull on the transverse processes of L1-. This client might end up with pain in the right sciatic nerve, or experience other pains produced by the compression of the discs. Over time, the discs might even bulge to the left because of the compression on the right. Healing the old bone break takes care of the condition, because it removes the protective muscle spasm and with this the compression of the discs, thereby making it possible for the biomechanics to realign and for the discs to heal and expand again.

I call the second degree of bone injury a "micro-fracture." The micro-fracture is a very fine fracture that does not go all the way through the bone. Consequently, no dislocation occurs. I have never seen an x- ray detect this type of fracture. Sometimes it produces a lot of pain at the location of the lesion. Frequently, this pain arises long after the actual injury happened. Micro-fractures have much the same consequences as those described for the incompletely healed, first-degree fractures.

In my treatments, I have seen a significant number of micro-fractures. They create all kinds of problems, especially after a number of years, because the protective muscle spasm and the compensation wear on the related parts of the body and generate symptoms over time. I have found many of these micro-fractures in the vertebrae. Nearly all of them were generated by accidents that put very strong compression onto the body of the vertebra. These micro-compression fractures can cause intense pain, usually at the location where the fracture occurred.

The third degree of bone injury is collapsed bone cells. Healthy bone cells show themselves to me with a round, slightly oval shape. When they are exposed to too much physical pressure, they can collapse, and then they look as flat as a pancake. Collapsed bone cells no longer bond strongly with their neighbors. Most often, you find collapsed bone cells only on the surface of bones, and most of the time this does not produce any symptoms. If bone cells collapse on the same plane that goes through the bone, they can cause instability in that bone. Sometimes areas of collapsed bone cells penetrate deeper into the bone and this can cause some pain or discomfort.

While we are on the subject of bone injuries, I would like to consider one more thing. Many broken bones are repaired with the help of metal hardware such as wires, plates or screws. If a piece of metal is in a bone, the body creates constant inflammation around it. This creates a little gap between the bone and the metal. (This does not seem to be the case with titanium implants.) The metal also disturbs the body's energetic field. If metal is present, the body has to make the adjustments necessary to maintain balance. Sometimes the body can't do this and it then rejects the metal.

Not too long ago I had screws and wires put in one of my legs after I broke two bones in an accident. I was concerned because my body did not feel too happy with the metal in there. I talked to it and told it that this was the only solution available to fix the bones in the right position. Rejecting the metal was therefore not an option. My body was not happy about this, but it left the metal in there, although I could feel the inflammation.

A friend of mine asked, "If you can treat people, why can't you treat the metal and make it more compatible with your body?"

I thought this was a good idea and so I started to figure out how to do it. I ended up adjusting the frequency of the metal to my body frequency. This instantly provided great relief.

Fifteen months later, I had surgery to remove the metal from my leg. The surgeon expected the procedure to take about twenty minutes. A day later I asked him how it went, and he said, "Man, I cannot understand what happened. Your bone grew right to the metal and locked it in there. I had a hell of a time getting it out. I have never seen anything like this before." He told me that it took him about forty-five minutes instead of twenty.

With the readjustment of the frequencies between the body and the metal, I think that the body did not consider the metal to be a big problem. Therefore, it did not try to stay away from it through the inflammation, and the bone grew right to the metal.

Today, I teach people with metal in their bodies how to adjust it to their body frequencies, because it needs to be done any time the frequency of the body goes up. I remember that I had to do mine about every four to five days. It also might be a good idea to stop this procedure some time before the surgery to remove the metal, in order to allow some inflammation to create a gap between the bone and the metal.

Central Nervous System Injuries

Injuries to the CNS are more common than you would think, because most of them do not cause any neurological symptoms. However, they do create a need for protection and so trouble will occur over time in other parts of the body. Without an understanding of how all this interconnects and the skill to read the energy body, it is unlikely that you will be able to connect a symptom somewhere else in the body to injured neurons in the CNS.

Let's examine the body's fundamental protection mechanisms for CNS injuries. To give you an idea of the way the neurons in the brain interconnect, I want to use a computer as an analogy. In a computer, the basic building blocks have three connectors. They are similar to transistors that work like switches. Only two responses to an input are possible: yes or no; or, in computer language, 0 or 1. Then this impulse goes to another unit where the procedure repeats itself. If one unit in a hard drive sends out chaotic impulses, it is likely that the hard drive will crash and become nonfunctional. This is due to the interconnections of all the building blocks.

A brain neuron has up to approximately 150 dendrites, which are the interconnections for input from other neurons. The axon of a CNS neuron, which is the wire for the outgoing input, can split into up to 500,000 fibers that connect to other neurons. Thus the interconnection of all the neurons in the brain and the traffic information exchange is much higher than in a computer. If one neuron sends chaotic impulses into the system, it could create a great disturbance. If a whole area of neurons does this, it might result in a system crash, or, in other words, death.

I am aware that the comparison of a brain and a computer is just an analogy, because they function quite differently. Nevertheless, it can give you the idea of how and why the body protects itself in case of damage to the central nervous system.

This is the situation when brain neurons are injured. The body instantaneously short-circuits all the affected neurons so that no impulse goes in, and especially not out, of them. Figure 12.1 shows how this works. You can see the neuron, dendrites and axon. The dashed lines are the short circuits that the body created. The body generates different pathways through the short circuits of the dendrites and axon of an injured neuron.

Chapter Twelve

A strong blow to the head can crush neurons on the outermost layer of the cortex. The short-circuiting happens instantaneously and, in the short run, the injury might not cause more than a big bump and a headache that lasts for a few days. In the long run, it has more serious consequences.

Every piece of tissue in the body connects to at least one nerve. If a piece of tissue is moved, the nerve to which it connects moves as well. This is not all. This nerve has a connection to a nerve in the spinal cord, which has a connection to a segment in the brain. All this shifts as a unit, with just the movement of this piece of tissue. We can make wonderful use of these interconnections in treatments to mobilize whole segments of tissue all the way through the spinal cord up into the brain.

When the injury occurs, the neurons in the affected area of the brain are immobilized and compressed, mostly due to the shock. After a while, they stick together and tighten. This means that the tissues take up less space. Suppose that some of these stuck-together neurons are a segment connected to the pectoralis minor. This means that every movement of this muscle pulls on a few of these neurons. Normally, they can glide over each other so that when the pectoralis minor moves, they can be pulled out and glide back in. With other neurons stuck to them, they can tear or suffer damage. The body knows this and it tightens the pectoralis minor and other related muscles so that this cannot happen. The result is compression in the anterior part of the thorax, with all the consequences for the body's biomechanics. It might show up as lower-back problems, knee or foot problems through the pull on the ilium, tennis elbow or carpal tunnel syndrome through the compression of the brachial plexus.

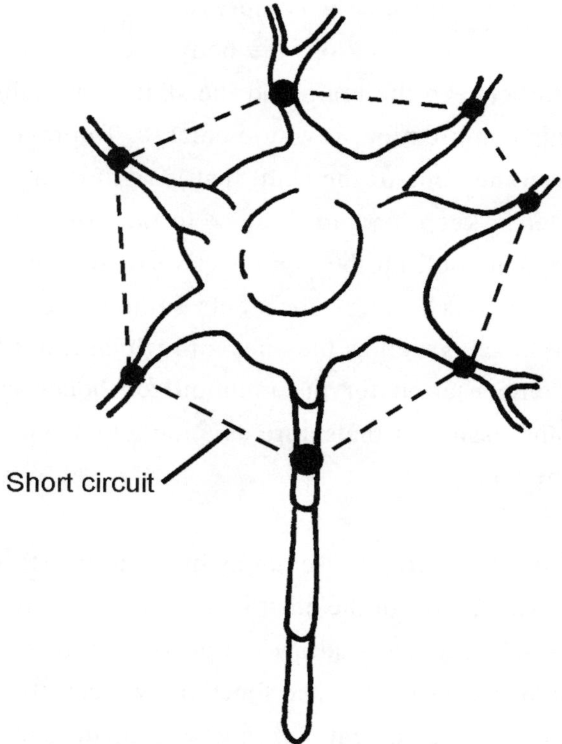

Fig. 12.1 The dots connected by dotted lines represent the short circuits of the dendrites and the axon of an injured neuron.

The body might not like any pull on these stuck neurons for other reasons, but I don't have a complete understanding about this yet. What I can see is that a pull on stuck neurons makes them fire. Firing means that they rapidly send out impulses that do not serve any purpose. The body then has to compensate for and balance this.

When neuronal tissue is compressed, it takes up less space in the brain. For some reason, the body needs the width of the gap of fluid between the brain and the skull to remain constant, but with this compression, it would enlarge. To prevent this, the body pulls in the bone of the skull that is right over the affected area in order to keep the gap as close to the original dimension as possible. This pull on the bone—let's say, one of the parietal bones—compresses at least one of its sutures and immobilizes the parietal bone as well as the ones into which it has been compressed. Compensation for the immobilized bones in the skull and the compression of the suture can now yield symptoms anywhere in the body.

CNS shock patterns are set up by different interfaces than the physical shock patterns of the other body tissues. The release of the shock is usually enough to allow the neurons to reconnect to the information of their structure and function by themselves. Within a few minutes after a treatment, the short circuits disappear from the treated area; the crushed neurons regenerate; and with this, the protective muscle spasms disappear. I know that this sounds spectacular, but I have now seen this happen hundreds of times. In the follow-up the body might ask for mobilization of the compressed neurons, and/or a mobilization of the compressed suture and/or a readjustment of the affected physiological biomechanics. More serious brain injuries generally produce a shock pattern, if not some damage, in the blood vessels of the affected area. Neurons need proper blood supply in order to regenerate. The shock release and the restructuring of the circulation in the brain usually go together with the restructuring of the neurons.

The neurons involved in this kind of injury do not seem to be dead, because they come back to life and function within just a few minutes. However, they seem capable of staying in this state of complete non-functionality after an injury for many years.

I don't have a lot of experience in treating people with strokes. I have treated a few, and I have found that if the treatment starts early enough—within about twenty-four hours of the stroke—and the stroke is not extremely strong, it is highly possible that all the symptoms will disappear. During the last year, I had a few clients who had strokes several days before I saw them. However, it was still possible to help the body to completely cure the symptoms with only a few treatments.

Now let's talk about spinal cord injuries. Most of the injured spinal cords that I have seen were not fully severed, though I did see one with about a thirty percent break.

The most promising scenario involves injury that occurs through a sudden compression of the spinal cord; for example, through the sudden and strong dislocation of one or more vertebrae. The compression of the spinal cord through vertebral movement immediately forces water out of the nerves and diminishes the diameter of the affected nerves. The shock shuts the area down and causes the body to stay in this mode of compression.

The tissue compression and shock severely reduce blood flow through the spinal arteries and veins, and the flow of cerebrospinal fluid in this area is likewise diminished. The impact and the resulting shock patterns produce a disconnection from most parts of the energy body that carry the information for structure and function of the damaged area. All this can cause the blockage of nerve impulses through the spinal cord.

Over time, the nerves in the spine become glued together due to the compression of the spinal cord. Nerves in the spinal cord as well as in the peripheral nervous system have to be able to move against each other. Every movement of body tissue produces movement in the related segment of the spinal cord as well. As we have seen in previous examples, the body, in its efforts to prevent damage, does not allow any pulling on nerves that are stuck to other nerves. The body tightens the related muscles to ward off potentially injurious movements.

Spinal cord injury can result in severe shock. In several instances, when I put my hands on the victim of a spinal injury, the first thing that the body communicated was, "I am dead." I was stunned when I first experienced this. I already had enough experience to know that this was not my imagination, so I stayed with it. Then I asked the body what had happened. All I got was the answer, "I am dead."

Finally, I told the body to do a little reality check; to look around and see if it was really dead. After a few seconds, the body realized that this was not the case and the treatment could start. As I see it, my talking was not the only thing that allowed the shift. Staying with the body in its belief that it was dead was essential. This was a treatment in itself—following the rules of RCT and just being with what is.

Treatment of spinal cord injury usually follows the same pattern. The first step is to help the body release as much shock as possible from the spinal cord and restructure the neurons. The second is to release shock from the spinal cord circulation and reestablish blood flow. Next, help get the nerves in the spinal cord to be able to move against each other and then get the cerebrospinal fluid moving. After that, go through the whole procedure over and over again. In between, you might have to make some biomechanical adjustments, especially to the sacrum. Sometimes brainstem tissue is damaged due to the sudden pull on the spinal cord and this needs to be addressed. Any broken vertebrae will also need attention. This represents a general picture of what you might find and by no means covers all the eventualities.

The first person with a spinal cord injury that I ever treated was paralyzed from the hips down. Her spinal cord was about thirty-percent severed. The accident happened three months before I started to treat her. After six treatments, she took her first steps, walking without any help.

It is my experience that it is possible to reconnect the body to its inherent ability to regenerate nerves in the CNS.

Internal Injuries

As long as an internal injury is not closed and the possibility of internal bleeding remains, the body needs to keep the shock in place. This helps compress the tissues and prevent internal bleeding. After an accident, most often the body asks for shock release in the affected areas first. Whenever this does not happen, I almost always find internal injuries in which bleeding must be prevented.

Internal injuries, wherever they take place in the body, leave scars. These scarred tissues contract over time and create a pull that can be felt all over the body. Scars in blood vessels can seriously narrow their diameter and reduce blood supply in the affected areas. If the body doesn't rebuild blood vessel walls strongly enough, it has to diminish circulation in the whole area in order to avoid putting too much pressure on the blood vessel.

The Central Nervous System

Much can be said about the central nervous system. In this book, I offer only the insights that I think are not commonly recognized, but can significantly facilitate the healing process.

Energetic Function

Western science's picture of brain function tells me that people think with their brains. This implies that the process of thinking occurs in the brain and we can figure it out by researching how brain matter behaves and what it does during thinking. I see this as a gigantic error caused mostly by the Western scientific paradigm.

I perceive thinking and feeling as purely energetic events. The brain connects thinking into the body. In conjunction with the hormonal glands, it also connects emotions into the body. The brain is a huge interface between the energy body and the physical body; i.e., between the mind and body. This is a function it has along with its physiological functions.

Every part of the brain serves as an interface that connects specific information from the energy body into the physical body. As it appears to me, the same places always connect the same information in everyone. For example, the same part of the right parietal lobe always connects the information about structure and function of the right lung into the body. All of these interfaces project themselves onto the surface of the skull.

I have decided to not draw and distribute a map of the interfaces. At this time I consider it best that you only work through these interfaces once you are an initiated practitioner. At this level of frequency you can just allow it to happen and it will be save whether you can read what you do or not. These interfaces also connect information below first frequency, but it takes an enormous level of skill and experience to utilize them for treatment. If it is your desire to acquire this level of skill, I am almost sure that you will be able to read them on your own once you are there.

On top of this, the body can magnify anything on the cranium as much as necessary. Let's say the interface of the heart projects itself onto a certain area of the skull. When you have to treat a specific aspect of the heart, the projection of the heart interface can cover the whole skull to show the aspect you need to know. Things are fluid in this way. If the body shows the interfaces on the same scale, it is my experience that you will always find the same things in the same places with few variations.

Don't forget that this is my way of doing RCT. Once you become a practitioner, you might find completely different ways to facilitate the connections, although the basic principles for how to do this remain the same.

Cerebrospinal Fluid (CSF)

I want to share some fascinating information about the cerebrospinal fluid (CSF). Most of the Western medical literature of which I'm aware finds the CSF only in the central nervous system, where it serves as a kind of buffer and shock absorber for the neuronal tissue, especially in the brain. Some researchers think that it also might supply some nutrition to the brain and help remove waste materials.

However, I experience CSF moving all through the body. It does this by flowing between the nerves and the nerve sheaths of the peripheral nervous system. The body seems to have a highly complex mechanism that insures that this fluid even gets into the innermost part of every nerve. Any kind of tissue compression seems to reduce the flow of CSF along the nerves and can even stop it. After a while, this might lead to nerve deterioration and many kinds of symptoms, from mild to total cessation of function. To me, the nerves then look as if they are dried out. They seem to shrink and shrivel like the skin of a mummy.

Commonly, after a treatment, when the tissues loosen up and the energy level is rising, the CSF also rushes back in. It seems to have an important role in re-energizing and restructuring compressed and damaged tissue.

I have observed a fascinating phenomenon involving CSF. I have seen CSF in the third ventricle moving out of three-dimensional reality into a higher dimension. It is recharged with energy there and then returns to the three-dimensional realm. The CSF appears to carry some specific information and energy that the nervous system needs to function.

You can treat CSF anywhere in the body. Treatment seems to polarize the fluid's molecular units, so that one end becomes positively and the other negatively charged. Treatments of the CSF can strongly impact body structure as well as the mind.

Compression of the Central Nervous System

This section mostly summarizes information that I have already covered here and there in other chapters. For your convenience, I am putting it all together in this one section.

The body has many rhythms. One purpose they serve is to keep the body mobile. Everything in the body is in constant, rhythmic motion. Let's look at the muscle rhythm, for example. All of your muscles elongate and contract at about six-to-ten cycles a minute. The organ rhythm moves the organs with approximately the same frequency. Connective tissue, the lymphatic system and the CNS each have a rhythm as well. The energetic system also has rhythms, which correlate with higher and higher frequencies of the energy body until they reach the breath of life, which, in my understanding is a rhythm that connects all life. All of these body rhythms do not seem to have the same frequency and phase. However, I feel that they are in harmony with each other in the same way that every note in a piece of music is in harmony with the others.

All the rhythms can be used for therapeutic work. I have not yet seen any RCT practitioner who facilitated connections by engaging these rhythms. This makes sense to me, because RCT connects information into the body, changing its structure and function in a way that might make these rhythms unnecessary at some point.

The rhythm of the CNS mobilizes all the nerves of the CNS all the time. For example, the spinal cord moves like a telescope, letting all the layers of neurons glide in and out of each other. If for any reason this movement is obstructed, in time they stick together more and more. I call this phenomenon "spinal cord fibrosis," a term I first learned at DCR.

As we have already learned, every pull from any cause or location in the body is transferred through the connective tissue and the nerves to every place in the body, including the CNS. This means that every tension in the body generates a pull on the related nerves of the CNS. (see "Injuries of the CNS" on page 182) The nerves in the brain and the spinal cord then become immobilized to a degree determined by the magnitude of the pull. As a result, the CNS rhythm cannot mobilize these nerves as much as usual. After some time, they become glued together, and can no longer glide over each other.

When the tissues that are located where the tension originally occurred loosen up through treatment, you will often find that you have to help the body loosen up the related structures in the central and peripheral nervous systems.

If through an accident or other reasons, the nerves in the CNS adhere, the tissues in the related area of the body tighten to prevent any kind of movement that could possibly pull on these stuck nerves, and tear them apart. This could damage the neuronal structure in the CNS. I feel that the body has other reasons for averting pulls on stuck CNS nerves, but right now I don't know exactly what they are. However, I have observed that when you stretch a nerve of the CNS, it starts to fire. This means that it puts out impulses unrelated to any reasonable function. The body has to compensate for and control these impulses to maintain balance.

Let's look at another impact of nerve compression in the brain. When neuronal tissues are compressed, they use up less space in the brain. The gap of fluid between the brain and the skull always has to be the same. With compression, this gap actually becomes bigger because the neuronal tissue in the brain shrinks. To prevent this from happening, the body pulls in the bone of the skull that is right over the affected area in order to keep the gap as close to the original dimension as possible. This pull on the bone pushes it against at least one other bone, compressing the sutures and immobilizing all the bones involved. This can cause symptoms anywhere in the body, because the body compensates for the immobilized bones in the skull and the compression of the sutures.

With all the types of diseases I have treated, I have often seen a significant amount of compression and immobility in the nerves of the CNS. This compression and immobility seems to be able to enclose a lot of symptoms in the CNS. This means that the symptoms your client should have according to the degree of degeneration that has already taken place in the CNS are not showing up. However, once you start the treatment and the CNS loosens up, your client can suddenly develop symptoms that he or she has never had before or had a long time ago.

Long-term, strong compression of the CNS can prevent any kind of symptom from manifesting, ranging from blood vessel spasm to old, incompletely healed injuries to un-integrated emotions. The compression of the nerves does not allow the information of certain dysfunctions to actually travel into certain parts of the brain and so into the awareness of the affected person. They are literally locked in that location in the body. If this is the case, occasionally during the course of the treatments, symptoms worsen significantly before they become better. Fortunately, this does not occur often. If it does occur, the aggravated symptoms usually do not last long. Most of the time, they subside in just a few days.

Meningitis and Encephalitis

It is very important that as a practitioner you know about the common aftereffects of meningitis and encephalitis. In both cases you will very likely find that the three layers of connective tissue around the CNS—the dura mater, the arachnoidea and the pia mater—are stuck together. Sometimes they are even glued to the nerves themselves or to the bones of the skull and/or to the bones of the skull and/or the spine. Encephalitis in particular can cause the nerves of the CNS to adhere. If untreated, these adhesions can remain for a lifetime.

This results in severe protective measures. The body does not allow any movements that could eventually pull on the stuck meninges or nerves. Most of the movements of the body move the meninges as well. Consequently, the body limits many things, especially its range of motion, even when the meninges are stuck only in a small place. Most of the time the range of motion throughout the entire body is limited not just movement only within a certain nerve segment. The degree of limitation depends on the number and size of the places where the meninges are stuck and how completely their three layers are glued together.

Immobilization of the meninges and the bones of the skull can cause strong emotional and mental stress. I have seen this many times, but I am still not able to give you the exact mechanics. It looks as if the brain neurons tighten, and consequently, the emotional system cannot fully interact with the physical body. This seems to create pressure from emotional energy in the interfaces between the emotional and the physical body and usually produces a fair amount of discomfort.

Helping the body to mobilize the meninges in these cases can cause dramatic changes within very short periods. It seems like essence is flooding back into the body and after this a person can look newly reborn.

Chapter Twelve

Multiple Sclerosis

Multiple sclerosis (MS) is the western medical name for a complex of symptoms caused by degeneration of the myelin sheaths in spinal cord nerves. In progressed MS, the degeneration sometimes occurs even in the brain and the peripheral nervous system. As far as I know, at this time, Western medicine does not understand the mechanics of MS and therefore offers no cure.

I have observed two basic structures associated with MS. The most common one is a chronic spasm in the spinal arteries. I want to share my idea about how this can set up MS symptoms. Artery walls consist of layers of connective and muscle tissue. Muscle tissue has the ability to contract. If the muscles of an artery wall contract, the artery's diameter and flexibility diminish (see "Circulation" on page 203). The diameter reduction is the most important factor here. In a chronic muscle spasm of the spinal arteries, the diameter of the arteries can become significantly smaller than it should be. If this goes beyond a certain point, nutrient supply to the spinal cord nerves is reduced. The body then has to decide which nerves to feed and which not to feed. It makes a lot of sense to cut the nutrient supply to the nerves that are not critical for survival. These are the motor nerves. Disintegration of the myelin sheaths of these nerves is a potential first impact of reduced nutrition, and this sets up the symptoms of MS. I cannot yet verify this model, but my experience shows that the symptoms of MS can vanish completely when the spinal arteries loosen.

In progressed MS the treatment becomes more complex. Arteries that are in spasm do not have their normal elasticity and tone. The body does not allow any kind of movement that would bend these arteries in a way that might harm them; they must be protected. The body tightens the involved muscles so that the patient can't bend his back beyond a certain point, which is determined by the degree of spasm in these arteries. I also see the neurons tightening, though I don't know how they do this. With all these factors present, the CNS rhythm finds it increasingly difficult to move the nerves in the spinal cord. Eventually, they become immobile, and, in time, adhere. This prognosis includes more and more nerves in the spinal cord as the MS progresses. Finally, it can go up into the brain and the peripheral nervous system.

You already know that when nerves stick together, the related muscles tighten to prevent a strain on them. As a result, the body can become increasingly stiff over time.

MS treatment usually progresses in repeated steps. The first step is to loosen the spinal arteries as much as possible, then to mobilize the nerves and get them to glide over each other again. Then you repeat this sequence over and over again. In between these steps, the emotional and mental body may show up for a treatment to reconnect the structures that created this condition in the first place. In progressed MS, you might also have to attend to the muscles to remobilize them.

A strong, energetic blockage in the center of the brain is the second structure that I have seen associated with MS. This can block the energy flow into the nerves of the spinal cord to such a degree that their myelin sheaths fall apart. For more information about this type of block, see "Strange Energy", starting on page 230.

I have never given more than a few treatments to someone with progressed MS, so I don't know how effective RCT is for this condition. However, I have worked on a few people with mild versions of this condition and they all became well, or at least much better, within just a few treatments.

Once the condition responsible for the degeneration of the myelin sheaths is cleared, the body can rebuild them in a comparatively short time.

If you are a RCT practitioner treating somebody with low-grade MS, it's good to be familiar with one more phenomenon. The CNS compression that accompanies MS seems to prevent symptoms from showing up to a degree that reflects the changes experienced by the CNS. The symptoms stay locked up in the compression. When this compression loosens, which usually happens after the first or second treatment, your clients can develop full-blown MS within twenty-four to forty-eight hours after the treatment. This can be alarming, but don't worry. My experience has shown that the symptoms completely disappear by themselves within a few days—though sometimes it can take up to two weeks. Knowing this, you can prepare your clients for what might come their way.

Seizures

Seizures have many causes, and they tend to differ from person to person. However, I have observed one circumstance in which seizures commonly arise: an energy buildup in the CNS that needs to be discharged. If it continues to build in the body, it can cause damage. For various reasons, the body cannot release this excess energy gradually. It can release it only when the energy reaches a certain threshold. The release then takes place all at once in one big swoop, and this produces symptoms, i.e., a seizure. The causes for this buildup vary from one person to another. Many people who accumulate excess energy in their CNS release it the moment that it occurs. Trembling and shaking are common ways to do this.

Depending on the location of the injury, seizures can also follow injuries and any kind of damage to the central nervous system. Remember that the body short-circuits damaged neurons. Damage to larger areas of the CNS, as in accidents or strokes, can produce areas where the neuronal short circuits do not work properly. Chaotic impulses might then leak out of the damaged areas or bypasses might work incorrectly. Consequently, energy can build and is ultimately released in one big surge, which we call a seizure.

Don't forget that in cases of injury to the CNS, the body is in an extreme emergency and has to react quickly. Therefore, it is not surprising that some of the short circuits and bypasses that the body sets up with this type of injury do not work perfectly.

Once the treatments bring down the threshold for the release of excess energy in the CNS, clients might develop involuntary movement and trembling, especially in the extremities. This simply means that the body now has found a less dangerous way to release this energy from the CNS. These symptoms frequently upset my clients more than the seizures they had not too long ago. However, when they understand that this indicates that they have taken a step towards healing, they usually calm down quickly.. If the threshold goes down further, these symptoms commonly disappear.

RCT has been very successful in helping people to heal from seizures.

Bones

There is one very interesting and important thing I want to share about bones.

Bones grow according to the lines of tension and pressure in the body. If any kind of tension is present due to dysfunction, it either pulls on the bones or compresses them. With dysfunctional tension, all movements put an abnormal strain on the bones.

Bones have a vivid metabolism, and from what I have heard, their structure is completely renewed about every ten-to-twelve years. Most of the people I have seen for treatment have had physiological tension for at least several years. As a result, their bones have gradually grown into a different structure. Bones can grow twisted, rippled or any way that you can imagine. You will see this at some point in your practice.

Let's use compression of nerve tissue as a typical example of how bones can become distorted. You learned earlier that compression shrinks neuronal tissue in the brain. The body then has to pull in the related bones of the skull, because it has to keep the fluid gap between the skull and the brain at the same width. In time, this pull can deform the bones so that they become bent, crooked, or compressed and manifest other distortions.

After RCT treatments, the brain tissue expands again. This could cause trouble, especially strong headaches, if the skull does not contain enough space for this expansion. Fortunately, this almost never occurs, because the body knows how far it can go at any time in the healing process. The body would not allow an expansion of the brain that the skull could not contain. When there is insufficient room for expansion, the bones of the skull have to be treated to loosen up the sutures and to get them back into their original shape. This creates the necessary space in the skull.

I find treatment of the internal structure of bones to be fascinating. During treatment, the bone cells disconnect from each other for a short period. The new information about structure and function connects, the bone cells shift to a new position and then they reconnect to each other in the usual way to create the solid bone structure. This process does not happen within the whole bone all at once. It progresses one layer at a time. This insures that the bone stays stable during the time of change.

A bone can change its internal structure and its shape rather quickly. I know this sounds far out, but I have treated a number of people with acute problems from twisted bones, and after the treatment, the symptoms have often disappeared within a few minutes.

Circulation

Circulation is the first thing that the body protects. Most people think that it's the brain, because it is so enclosed in the skull and the spine and is so fragile. This is not my experience. A lot of brain tissue can die before a person checks out. If even a small portion of a major artery—in the CNS or the heart, for example—gets injured or clogged, an immediate threat of death or crippling arises. The body therefore does everything to protect the circulatory system before anything else.

Spasm of the blood vessels is one of the most common circulatory problems that I treat in my practice. The walls of blood vessels consist of several layers of connective and muscle tissue, which have the ability to contract and relax. Let me give you an example of the consequences of a blood vessel spasm.

Imagine that the right subclavian artery is in spasm. One of the effects of an artery in spasm is decreased elasticity. In stronger spasms, the blood vessel can become fairly stiff. The diameter of the blood vessel also diminishes and less blood can then pass through. When a blood vessel is in spasm for a long time, it can become rigid and stiff and clog more easily.

Certain movements of the arm and the chest bend the subclavian artery. When it is in spasm, bending it beyond a certain degree can harm the artery's tissues. The body will never allow this to happen. It tightens all the necessary muscles to prevent these movements. If a person with this condition tries to bend his right arm backwards, he can only do it to a certain degree before he starts rotating his body at the hip.

The body is extremely serious about protecting an artery like this. Nothing can force a movement that could harm this artery. I once saw a client whose shoulder was completely frozen because of a strong spasm of the subclavian artery. It was beautiful to watch how, after the treatment of this artery, his shoulder relaxed and dropped down more and more every minute. With spasms of a subclavian artery, problems show up through the protective muscle spasm. This pulls on other areas of the body, causing additional problems. This basic sequence of events is valid for all arteries.

Muscle spasm protects not only blood vessels in spasm, but also most any part of the body, including emotions and memories that have been stored there. As a consequence, most of the time RCT practitioners don't treat the body parts that hurt, but rather the place where the pain actually originates. One exception is accidents and injuries, as long as they are not too old.

Blood-vessel spasms in the brain can seriously diminish circulation throughout the whole body. I had a client once whose circulation was only fifty percent of what it should be. In treatment, I found that one artery in the circle of Willis was in a strong spasm. The body had to diminish general circulation to reduce pressure on this artery. The treatment removed the spasm from the artery, and, within a few minutes, his circulation was back to 100 percent.

Clogged arteries or veins, as well as stuck blood clots, are another problem that you might face. When I was in training with DCR, I had a client with a thrombophlebitis in his right calf. At this time, I did not know whether I could treat this or how to proceed. I was concerned that it might loosen up the blood clot and cause major damage. I asked one of my teachers about this, and she said: "As long as you go indirectly, you will be safe. In twenty years, I have never killed anybody." Eight years of practice have shown me that she was right.

In any kind of indirect technique (see Chapter 8), and especially in RCT, you let the body do whatever needs to be done by itself. The body consciousness knows about blood clots and other possible hazards and will not do anything that could endanger it. That's one of the beauties of indirect techniques.

Chapter Twelve

Next I want to talk about the heart. Some time ago, I read research that stated that the heart's pumping power is too small by far to move the blood all the way out through the blood vessels and back to the heart. However, I see a rhythmic movement in the blood vessels that functions like a pumping mechanism and helps the blood to move along.

The heart seems to set the rhythm for the whole body. When every cell synchronizes with this rhythm, you feel happy in your body—emotionally, mentally and physically. Feelings of joy, love and compassion seem to synchronize the cells with the rhythm of the heart. I think that joy is the most important fuel for maintaining health. In treatments with RCT, you can connect and synchronize the whole body or parts of it with the heart's rhythm.

Heart attacks are still one of the main causes of death in modern society. I want to make one addition to all the research that has been done. Though they don't know it, many people have little cracks in the tissue of their hearts.. I am not sure how these cracks appear, but I think that tightness in the heart muscle, followed by sudden movements or blows to the heart area, can produce them.

If a crack becomes too large, it can pose a threat to the heart muscle. The body stabilizes this area by creating a heart attack exactly at the place of the crack. When the related coronary artery goes into spasm, the consequent lack of circulation causes the heart tissue to die and forms a scar. These scars look as if somebody sewed over the crack to stabilize it.

Today, most allopathic medical professionals see clogged arteries as the major physical reason for heart attacks, and a certain type of cholesterol as the offending agent. Bad diet and lack of exercise are generally considered primary causes of increased levels of cholesterol in the blood.

Recently, I read about research that precisely confirmed one of my observations on the cause of heart attacks. The researchers found that heightened levels of blood cholesterol are not to blame for clogged arteries. Instead, they discovered that inflammation in the tissue of the artery walls is what allows the cholesterol to attach to them in the first place. This raises a question about what leads to inflammation of the blood vessel walls.. I think that the body's self-protective mechanisms, described in the section above, are the primary cause (see "Body Protection" on page 156).

According to what I can see, the change in tissue structure starts when the arteries store emotions beyond a certain degree. Integrating these emotions allows the inflammation in the walls of the affected blood vessels to heal. In turn, this makes them much less prone to clogging.

RCT can successfully treat cracks in the heart muscle, as well as scars from heart attacks. I do not know whether the scars really disappear or not. When they heal, and the related symptoms vanish, I simply cannot see them any more.

Lungs

When the lungs need protection, the whole body usually experiences major tension. Consequently, if the lungs need treatment, this usually shows up first. Let's examine the main reasons for lung protection.

In my experience, pneumonia is number one. Every bout of pneumonia leaves scarred tissue in the affected lung. In a case of light pneumonia, scars only form on the surface. With a stronger case, the scars extend deeper into the lungs and adhesions often remain between the lung and the pleura. Due to the body structure that most of us have at this time, these adhesions and scars remain for a lifetime if untreated.

The number-two reason for lung protection is a physical impact that puts the lung into shock and can also leave cracks in its tissues. I have found the most severe shock patterns and lung compressions in cases where the lungs collapsed.

Back to number one. Scars tend to contract over time. This means that scarred lungs become more compressed and inflexible. A lot of body movements pull on the lungs, which increases the potential for straining the scarred tissue and generating further damage. Therefore, the body has to protect the lungs. This protection shows up mainly through tightening of the rib cage. The major muscles involved are the pectoralis minor, the latissimus dorsi, the rhomboideus and the scaleni anterior, medius and posterior. These muscles pull the rib cage medially (towards the midline of the body) and cranially (towards the head). The goal of the body is to tighten and immobilize the rib cage and push the lung cranially as much as necessary. The lung is most protected in this position. The more protection the lung needs, the stronger this protective muscle spasm will be.

The body protects the adhesions between the lung and the pleura as well as cracks in its tissue in the same way, i.e., by tightening the same muscles to prevent any movement that might pull on the adhesions or cracks.

The muscle spasm that protects the lungs has a number of consequences. I'll only talk about the three major ones.

If the lung is moved upward through the protective muscle spasm, at some point, it starts pushing onto the brachial plexus. The brachial plexus contains all the nerves that supply one arm. The typical symptoms of this brachial plexus compression are tennis elbow and carpal tunnel syndrome. So far, brachial plexus compression caused by the lung has been the origin of carpal tunnel syndrome or tennis elbow in almost every case that I've treated. The few exceptions involved tissue compression that was the direct result of an injury to the arm.

The anterior, medial and posterior scalene muscles extend from the transverse processes of C2 through C7 (cervical vertebrae numbers 2 – 7) to the first two ribs on the same side. When these muscles go into spasm, they pull the first two ribs up and the transverse processes of C2 through C7 down. This creates a compression of the discs, usually more strongly on one side than the other. The disc compression might lead to anything from neck stiffness, to neck pain, to bulging discs. This is another situation that demonstrates that symptoms don't necessarily reflect the location of the problem. In fact, the protective muscle spasm sets up the symptoms.

The muscles that protect the lung generate a strong pull on the ilium on the same side. You usually find an up-slipped ilium that can also be rotated around its vertical or horizontal axis. The presence of rotation and its degree depend on the specific way the body has set up the lung protection. Amongst other problems, this can easily lead to knee problems, because of the misalignment of the sacro-iliac joint on this side, which in turn pulls on the femur and causes misalignment of the knee.

My experience has shown that lung scars, adhesions and cracks respond very well to RCT treatments.

DNA

DNA is constructed from physical matter. Therefore, information in the energy body holds the blueprint for it. This means that RCT can treat the structure of the DNA, just as it treats any other body structure. DNA treatment is no more difficult than other treatments. From what I have seen, every treatment with the second frequency and above changes the structure of the DNA.

DNA treatments often show up in conditions like arthritis, rheumatism or pemphigus—conditions where the immune system attacks its own tissue. Interestingly, a DNA treatment frequently precipitates deep relaxation throughout the body within a short time.

I have also used RCT successfully to treat genetically based conditions that existed from birth.

The Growth Process

The energy body of a person who incarnates on planet Earth exists before conception. This means that all the possibilities for this lifetime are already present, including their potential expressions in space and time, which means the shape, structure and function of their physical body. The choices an individual makes along the path determines which of these possibilities manifests at certain times in his life. Some things are inevitable, while others are not.

Remember that the energy realms exist beyond space and time. Therefore, although all the possibilities for one lifetime are available in the energy body even before birth, here in time and space, they have to unfold according to the laws of this realm. This is what we call growth. If we look into the structure of the energy body, we can see that all the information for the growth process is in there.

Every time period seems to have its own templates that hold the information for body structure and function. For example, one template might govern the growth process from age two to two-and-a-half. This specific set of information determines the shape, structure and function of the body during this period. At the end of that period, it disconnects from the body and the next template—let's say for age two-and-a-half to three—connects, and so on. The pituitary gland appears to govern the timing process. Interestingly, the pituitary gland also produces the growth hormone.

I have seen problems arise with this process when information between the templates for different ages bleeds through. For example, the information for structure and function for the ligaments of one leg for age three connects at age two instead. The consequence can be a very instable and abnormally limber leg, because the ligaments are way too long for it at the time. It is also possible for information about structure and function for a certain part of the body to connect later than it is supposed to or to connect incompletely. It is then too small or underdeveloped.

I have seen problems with the growth process most often in horses that are bred for racing (see "Horses" on page 260). In horses with the so-called "wobbler syndrome," I often see that the spinal channel could not keep up with the growth of the spinal cord. This leads to compression of the spinal cord and to loss of coordination in the movement of the horse's legs. The same problem can occur when information about the development of the cervical spine does not connect completely. The consequence can be instability in the cervical spine that can also cause spinal cord compression. RCT Treatments have proven to be very efficient in getting the growth process back in order and helping the body eliminate the associated symptoms.

Infection

It is considered common knowledge that many micro-organisms—viruses, bacteria, fungi, parasites and so on—have the potential to cause disease. All of my experience tells me that this cannot be the case. First, I'll explain my position theoretically and then give you examples from my experience.

Remember that everything in the physical body is interconnected. A pull on the big toe influences the brain, the organs and everything else in the body, including the immune system. Second, as we saw in Chapter 9, it's almost impossible to isolate one, well-defined cause for any condition. Every cause has a cause, has a cause and so on.

Can we then actually find a final cause for infectious diseases? I don't think that a final cause exists. Consider these two things—the interconnection of everything in the physical body and the causal chains— and it becomes clear that the approach via cause and effect is inappropriate for understanding how the body functions and heals.

An Extended Understanding of Body Structure and Function

In holistic medicine, we see the body and the mind as the unit that they are and approach understanding and healing in this way. This does not mean that we exclude physical examination and the information that it provides. We just put this information into a different context.

As far as I understand, no germ has ever caused any kind of disease. The environment of the body has to be in a state that allows germs to connect; otherwise they cannot take hold in the body. Consequently, we do not contract pneumonia because we are exposed to a certain germ. It manifests because the environment in our lungs has already changed in a way that allows the germs to multiply.

Some simple evidence supports this. The immune system is perfect. This means that as long as it is working at its full capacity, we won't become seriously ill from any kind of microorganism. Therefore, is the pneumonia due to exposure to the germ or dysfunction of the immune system? In addition, why is the immune system not fully functional?

In my eight-year practice of classical homeopathy, I treated a large number of people with acute diseases. Many times when I made a home visit to a very sick patient and gave him a remedy, he felt significantly better within about fifteen minutes. The remedies that I gave were pure lactose on the physical plane and held the remedy's information on the energetic plane. How can the germ theory be accurate? If it were, the body would have had to kill off millions of germs in a few minutes, helped only by a purely energetic remedy.

As I understand it, the remedy causes a shift in the structure of the body's environment and then the body simply disconnects from the germ. With this type of treatment, it appears that the body does not have to kill or destroy invaders. They simply die by themselves, because they suddenly find themselves in an environment where they can no longer survive. All that is left for the body to do is rid itself of the debris.

The average healing time for pneumonia, once I found the correct remedy, was two-to-three days. It was the same with ear infections, mononucleosis, tonsillitis and so on. In the twenty-one years that I have been a practitioner, I have had very few cases where we were unable to facilitate the cure of an infectious disease with classical homeopathy or RCT. After more then one year of practicing both RCT and homeopathy simultaneously, I found RCT to be a much more effective tool for me, and I stopped practicing homeopathy.

I have treated many people suffering from infectious diseases with RCT. These treatments seem to follow a general pattern. If necessary, the body wants to take care of the underlying structure of the disease first. This usually means facilitating the connection of the emotional and mental bodies, which helps the body integrate the emotions and thought forms that have contributed to the creation of this experience. Then the body asks to have the immune system activated. Many times this activation includes a shift in the structure of the DNA that allows the immune system to connect to more of its capacity lying dormant as a potential within the energy body. If my understanding is correct, a treatment like this makes the immune system stronger than it usually is in people. The activation often allows the body to take care of even very potent and acute diseases within a spectacularly short time. If an acute, infectious disease has a strong and deeply-rooted emotional component, the healing can take more time. In the case of a strong acute disease with a deep-rooted emotional component, it can be helpful to resort to suppressive measures, such as antibiotics and steroids to give the body more time to integrate the related emotions.

One example from my practice can give you an idea of how powerfully these activations can affect the body. I had a client who had traveled to Africa and brought home an intestinal infection that caused strong symptoms. Nobody was able to determine what germ it was and none of the remedies she received worked. After the first treatment, which consisted of the activation of the immune system, most of her symptoms vanished, and the second treatment a week later took care of the rest.

I have observed one more infectious disease mechanism that I want to share. As a healthcare practitioner, I think that it is extremely important that you know about this. When the body is subject to an infectious disease, the immune system might not be able to take care of everything at the same time. As result, it encloses certain parts of the infection within connective tissue and takes care of them when it has the capacity to do so. I am not exactly sure how this process of encapsulation works, but I have clearly seen the body do this. I have also seen that it takes a lot less immune system capacity to control an encapsulated part of an infection than to control and heal an acute aspect. The encapsulation process is particularly extensive when the immune system response has been suppressed through allopathic medication, such as antibiotics or steroids.

Lack of awareness of this mechanism has caused vast parts of the planet's population, who have been exposed to allopathic treatment, to become chronically ill or die. Let's explore why. When a child, for example, suffers from acute pneumonia, almost every allopathic physician treats it with antibiotics. This causes a certain amount of the infection to be locked up in connective tissue. These aspects of the disease stop creating symptoms, but it takes a continuous toll on immune capacity to keep them controlled and encapsulated. In addition, the tissues that hold the infection can only carry out their original function to a limited degree.

After allopathic treatment, the child's disease symptoms subside within two weeks and she is declared healthy. Six months later her body, having recovered to a degree, goes ahead and opens up the tissues that hold the infection, in order to complete its healing permanently. The infection then emerges from the connective tissue so that the immune system can eliminate it. A client's former symptoms usually flare up as part of this process, and this is the case with the little girl. She then goes to the doctor, who gives her antibiotics again to get a handle on the infection, hopefully once and forever.

The strength of the immune system determines how many times this or any client will go through this cycle. At some point, the immune system becomes so weak, that it can no longer heal the encapsulated infection. This means that the infection remains in the tissues, with all the negative consequences described above. This situation can lead to almost any kind of chronic disease that you can imagine.

Homeopaths have known about this mechanism for about 200 years. People who receive homeopathic treatments generally remain a lot healthier. As I understand it, this widespread suppression of the immune system has led to an incredible epidemic of chronic diseases.

Once you understand this mechanism, it is not that hard to distinguish between an acute infection and the healing process that we just discussed. With acute disease, the patient's energy level lowers significantly. He feels sick, and to the practitioner, his energy body feels sick as well. If you look at these later or delayed stages of the healing process, this is usually not the case. The energy level generally changes just a little bit, if at all, and the eyes have their usual sparkle and clarity. An experienced practitioner most often has no problem distinguishing between these two conditions. People who have some sensitivity to their own bodies can also do this. They might say: "I don't feel good, but I don't feel that I am sick."

It's also important to know that infection can scar tissues and glue them together. These scars and adhesions often remain indefinitely if untreated. Be alert to this possibility when you treat people who have a history of infections, especially in the organs or the CNS. Some people can raise their frequency enough to allow these scars and adhesions to heal by themselves. This ability exists potentially in everybody and can be activated.

I know that many questions surround the concepts of infectious disease and the model that I propose. I can't fully answer these questions in the context of this book. Each individual attracts germs and heals the consequences in different ways and for different reasons.

Many of the questions also concern hypothetical situations or collective phenomena, such as epidemics, or the exposure of indigenous peoples to microorganisms that are totally new to their physiologies. A group or collective reacts like a body, where each individual is like one cell of that body. Therefore, every incidence involving a collective being hit by an epidemic would need to be examined separately, because it would most likely present unique circumstances.

I am excluding the topic of HIV/AIDS in this section because I lack experience with it.

Vaccination

This topic is a hot iron, because so much fear surrounds it and so much disinformation has been widely spread since vaccinations were first introduced. This might be shocking news for some of you, but I think that it is better to wake up with a shock than to continue suffering body damage without even knowing how the damage occurred.

I will not talk much about the lies, as well as the withholding and distortion of information that has taken place regarding the benefits and risks of vaccination. I'll provide a snapshot of the situation, based on two good books about this issue by Neill Z. Miller: "Vaccines, Are They Really Safe and Effective?" Or the more extensive version "Vaccine Safety Manual" (www.thinktwice.com). After this, I'll contribute a few observations from my daily practice.

First of all, no evidence exists that vaccinations have ever contributed in any way to the decline of the illnesses that they are supposed to prevent. These illnesses were already on the decline before vaccinations started and they did not decline any faster after the introduction of vaccines.

Vaccinations do not even come close to providing the protection claimed.

Vaccines are not as safe as their proponents promise. In fact, research has shown that they can cause everything from allergic reactions to autism, paralysis and death. Cases of vaccine-related illnesses are common, not exceptional. Vaccines have also done a lot of harm not yet attributed to them. Briefly, it looks as if the damage from many vaccines is much greater than the negative effects of the diseases that vaccines purport to eliminate. Neill Z. Miller's books expand on all these points.

In the nine years since I became aware of this situation, I have noticed that every vaccination produces little pockets of infection in the brainstem as well as in the nerve plexi of the gut. It appears to be a chronic condition that, in most people, the body cannot currently heal by itself. This has extremely far-reaching consequences.

First I want to discuss the function of the nerve plexi in the gutt. The gut's innervation is far more complex than needed to produce its simple peristaltic motion. Research conducted in the Western medical community has shown, that these nerves are organized like the brain and match its complexity and capacity. They found that the "gut brain" is a real brain and that human beings actually have two interconnected brains. The research also found that the gut brain has the ability to override many decisions of the "head brain". When I use the term "brain", I am referring to the brain in our heads. When I talk about the abdominal brain, I use the term "gut brain".

I will start with the physical level. Every nerve impulse that goes from the brain to the body, and from the body to the brain, has to go through the brainstem. Compression here limits the amount and intensity of impulses that can go back and forth. The central nervous system is the main energy conductor in the body. Compression in the brainstem thus limits the amount of energy that can go from the brain into the body and back. The amount of damage in the brainstem determines the degree of limitation. Brainstem compression also limits the amount of information about body structure and function that is supposed to pass from the interfaces in the brain down to the related parts of the body. If the body has to operate its systems with a limited amount of energy and information, in the long run, this can cause any kind of symptom we can imagine. When young, the body compensates more easily for all this. As we grow older, the consequences can be more severe.

In nearly everyone who comes for treatment who has been vaccinated, I have seen the brainstem show up at some point for restructuring due to vaccine related damage.

I have seen sudden outbreaks of the infection in the brainstem. If a person has already had a number of vaccinations and adds another one, it can be the straw that breaks the camel's back. The body can no longer contain the infection. I have seen this result in acute brain and spinal cord infections in adults, children and animals. I have seen asthma, skin conditions, allergies, paralysis, week immunity, indigestion, autoimmune conditions, almost any symptom known to man linked to vaccinations.

I have also frequently observed that vaccinations usually have a strong influence on personal development, especially during childhood. To understand this please recall that the central nervous system is one of the major interfaces that connects thinking and feeling into the body. The same is true for the gut brain. Now imagine what happens if parts of this interface are no longer available for this function due to chronic inflammation as a result of vaccination. The child's personality shifts. It feels like, less of the child is available. Consequently the child is suddenly not as bright or alert, almost as if he has dimmed or somehow altered. Some parents notice this change, but few relate it to recent shots. If this affects a child more intensely, often times it is called autism. Independent research strongly suggests a correlation between vaccination and autism.

Homeopaths have always warned against vaccination. Because of their perspective and treatment approach, classical homeopaths have always been able to link many more conditions to the effects of vaccination than today's scientific research can or is willing to do.

They understand that if a person becomes acutely ill, let's say with an infection, his immune system response causes his symptoms, not the germs that invaded his body. The stronger the immune system, the stronger the response it can produce. Therefore, a person who produces a 104° fever during an infection is fairly healthy. If somebody is chronically ill, the body can no longer become acutely ill, because it is using too much of its capacity to stabilize the chronic conditions. Vaccinations create chronic conditions, making it impossible for the body to experience acute illness. This is how many homeopaths understand the implications of vaccination.

A tremendous amount of evidence validates this point of view. We do not have epidemics of acute diseases anymore, but we do have a gigantic epidemic of chronic diseases. I do not have to use statistics to prove this. When I was a kid, people with allergies were exotic. Today, people with no allergies are exotic. I can extend this observation to nearly any kind of chronic disease. How many adults do you know who can produce acute conditions with over 104° fever? In twentyone years of practice, I have seen only a few few.

Aconitum Napellus can produce extremely acute symptoms. About 100 years ago, it was one of the most commonly used remedies in homeopathy for acute childhood diseases. In all my years of practice, I have never seen anybody produce these symptoms.

The good thing about acute diseases is that the body takes care of them quickly; or sometimes the disease takes care of the body. A chronic disease by definition is one that the body is unable to heal by itself. The body can only stabilize itself and try to balance the potential for dysfunction in the least damaging way.

I want to make it clear that I do not recommend either for or against vaccination. You need to learn to take complete responsibility for your own health. In order to do this, you need valid information. In regard to vaccination, I consider it one of my jobs to share information to the best of my ability.

Do not quit getting vaccinated because somebody tells you that vaccines damage your health. Find out for yourself what is real and what is not. Then find the kind of decision for which you can take responsibility. If you can't handle a situation in which your child gets polio and becomes crippled, and you will blame yourself for the rest of your life for not having him vaccinated, you'd better have him vaccinated. However, you could also find yourself in a crisis when you do have your child vaccinated and he or she becomes chronically ill, autistic, paralyzed or dies shortly thereafter. To make such an important decision and feel good about it, you have to become informed.

If you decide vaccination is not for you or your children, I highly recommend that you find out what treatment modalities can deal with polio, tetanus, whooping cough and so on. Classical homeopathy and RCT are both quite effective and more are out there. Have a backup team of good practitioners that can provide help when you need it.

Almost every class I teach asks: "How can such important information be suppressed or distorted for so long? If vaccinations cause such serious health damage, why is so much effort put into promoting them worldwide?"

I will keep the answer short.

From all the data I have available, I understand that this planet is ruled by a small group of people, who control most of its money and resources. They are absolutely unknown to the public. They also largely control the media. The media puts out material that is designed to brainwash its consumers. This ruling group knows a lot about energy and how to use it for control. The goal of all this is to manipulate the thought patterns of vast parts of the population. It seems to be their agenda to gain complete domination over this planet. They need to keep people limited and busy so that they don't wake up and understand what is going on.

The group's main tools in the health field are vaccinations and the mercury in dental fillings. These tools keep people more-or-less chronically ill all their lives. Yes. You hear me correctly. I think this has been done to humankind on purpose.

I could fill another book with evidence about this plan, including the murder of inventors of free-energy machines, the withholding of gasoline-saving devices for cars, the suppression of information about easy-to-apply and inexpensive life-saving treatment devices and so on. A number of authors go into these issues: Drunvalo Melchizedek, David Icke and others. If you think this makes sense, you can start reading about it. Due to the sensitive nature of this issue, anything you read about it might contain distorted information. If you want to see for yourself whether all this is true, I recommend first, that you stay away from the media completely; and second, that you develop your ability to discern truth from non-truth.

Growing up in Western society, you only learn one way to look for truth, which is to gather and evaluate information, by some theoretically objective standards. I know of another one that is at least as good. Learn to listen to yourself and your feeling about things, and to trust that more than anything or anyone else. In time, you can simply feel the information that comes to you inside yourself, and know whether it is real or unreal. Western education purposefully disconnects us from this ability.

One can now go ahead, collect information and wallow in world's "evil". I do not find this to be an attitude that facilitates change. I think that a more efficient question to ask oneself is: "What is the challenge this provides for us? What is in us that led to a creation like this?". One thing that I clearly see, allowed this to happen is, the Western population's surrender of responsibility for their health to the medical establishment. I know few people at this juncture who educate themselves about medical procedures before receiving them, and who trust their inner knowledge more than their doctor. On the issue at hand, the information on vaccines is readily available. It is up to us to take responsibility for those in our care and ourselves.

This is all I want to say about this subject. If you decide you want to have a closer look at it, remember that whatever you put your attention on grows. Maintain your focus on the solution, rather than the problem. Awakening to these things is only helpful if you have enough love to stay with the facts and minimize judgment and anger. Then you will be part of the solution, not the problem.

Cancer

Cancer grows in places in the body that have been cut off from the energy body for a long time. The cells in an excised area no longer receive information about how to function in harmony with the body as a whole. They can function normally for a while from memory, but they lose this memory over time. Finally, they are left with the instructions that they have inside themselves as cells, and these say just to grow.

The immune system does not step in and eliminate cancer cells, because it does not recognize them. Since the area was cut off from the energy body, the energy body does not recognize its existence.

From what I have seen, cancer usually has a strong emotional component. It does not develop overnight, but takes a long time, usually many years. The growth of tumors is just the final stage.

I have observed that before tumors manifest in an area of the physical body, the DNA in these places starts to deteriorate. You can potentially develop the ability to read energy to the degree that you perceive this. I can see it at times years before the tumors appear. This process starts in the DNA's energetic templates, and then moves into the dna itself. Finally the body starts growing tumors. In my experience, healing the premiliminary stage of cancer is much faster and easier than beginning treatment after the tumors manifest physically.

From this perspective, healing must clearly include the related structures of the mind. Surgery can give the body some relief, but it does not address the conditions that caused the tumors to grow in the first place. I personally see chemotherapy and radiation as the most barbaric things that can be done to people with cancer. From what I have witnessed, they are not efficient treatments for cancer. Only rarely, I have seen a very short sequence of chemotherapy "buy" the body more time for the healing process.

RCT treatment for people who are on chemo or radiation has to be handled with extreme care. Once the body experiences RCT's effectiveness, it will most likely produce a strong adverse reaction to the chemotherapy and/or radiation. Due to the toxicity, the body goes into contraction mode during chemotherapy or radiation. With RCT, it opens, and the body usually can't switch back and forth between these two styles of operating. This is another reason why RCT does not mix well with chemotherapy and radiation. However, I have observed that, if you are strong and clear enough as a practitioner, you can set your intention such that you can support the body with RCT treatments even during chemo-therapy or radiation.

I will not talk about the success rate of RCT in treating cancer here because, as I have already discussed, the outcome of a treatment like this can never be determined in any way. I do not want to raise hopes that might not be fulfilled or discourage hopes where a strong possibility for healing exists.

Detoxification

To understand this chapter's importance, please remember that Chapter 9 described why a practitioner's beliefs influence a treatment's effect.

Modern science has always laughed at alchemy, although few scientists have known what alchemy is. It is assumed to be the forerunner of modern chemistry and to have consisted mostly of weird guys who tried to make gold. Those weird guys actually existed, but their description of alchemy was a distortion of the truth. Alchemy had and still has a level of knowledge about the structure of matter and the process of transformation about which contemporary science can only dream.

In the old alchemical literature, it was common knowledge that a living system, like the body of an animal or human being, can perform transmutations from one element into another at low energy. Physics knows how to do this to a small degree but only by applying very high energy such as particle acceleration or exposure to radioactivity. As far as I know, Western science considers this kind of low-energy transmutation to be impossible.

A man named Louis C. Kervran researched this area at the beginning of the twentieth century. The first thing he found was that if any kind of calcium is withdrawn from the diet of chickens, they still lay eggs, but these eggs don't have shells. He also observed that chickens like to eat a kind of silicon in crystalline form, which is called Glimmer in German. He started adding this to their diet. After they ate it, they laid eggs with a calcium shell. Somehow, their bodies were able to transmute silicon into calcium.

Kervran made another interesting observation when he was working with people who did hard physical labor in the African desert. It was his job to find the most suitable diet for that environment. In his research, he found that when people sweat a lot, they need more salt in their diets. What we refer to as dietary salt consists mostly of sodium chlorate. When he analyzed the workers' sweat, he found that it mostly consisted of potassium chlorate. He concluded that their bodies were capable of transmuting sodium into potassium. According to Kervran, the body does this because this transmutation uses up energy and so cools the body down. I have something to add to this as well.

I started studying alchemy around 1985, so the knowledge of low-energy element transmutation was nothing strange to me. Before I began to use and understand RCT, I had already started to let go of my belief that a person has to suffer in order to heal. It became increasingly clear to me that healing can be easy. In this context, I also let go of the belief that the body has to excrete toxins in order to remove them.

People who use or offer alternative health care commonly believe that health requires the elimination of toxins, and that the body has to excrete them either through the digestive tract, urinary tract, skin and so on. This belief also includes the idea that a really good healing is followed by a strong detoxifying reaction. The client feels terrible and everything that comes out of him stinks like hell.

RCT treatments usually do not produce any signs of detoxification. For a few years, I worked closely with an expert in toxicity diagnostics and detoxification. She saw a lot of my clients. During the course of RCT treatments, she found that their toxicity levels decreased steadily, without any external signs of detoxification, or the use of any other kind of treatment that is known to facilitate detoxification.

In my experience, every toxin in the body can leave without causing any kind of symptom. I see my clients breaking down or transmuting their toxins into something that either flushes out easily, is completely harmless or may even be useful for the body.

I have observed that most people are not toxic due to exposure to toxins. If you look at people who are exposed to the same toxins, some store them in their bodies and some don't. Certainly, an exposure to huge amounts of toxins can overload someone's system and break down the body's natural way of processing them. Yet some people tolerate huge amounts of toxins without any major symptoms, even with large stores of them in their bodies, while others hold on to everything to which they are exposed and react to it violently.

It appears to me that toxicity is about an affinity to certain toxins. This means that the body does not let go of them; it stores them somewhere in the tissues. I also find people whose energy level is too low to get rid of the toxins they encounter. In both cases, I think that detoxification through the use of purifying substances does not make a lot of sense.

If an affinity for certain toxins is not removed from the system, the body stores the same toxins again and any detoxification process only provides temporary relief. When the body does not have enough energy to process toxins normally, initiating a process of detoxification only produces further strain and does nothing to enhance the body's ability to deal with toxicity.

I am not against detoxification techniques. I simply want to offer an extended understanding about this. Since not everybody has access to RCT treatments, detoxification can help the body relieve symptoms and use its resources in a better way.

Toxins are largely held in areas in the body with low energy. With RCT, the energy body can reconnect to those locations, the frequency goes up and then the toxins cannot stay. RCT can also remove affinities to toxins and remind the body of its ability to transform toxins into harmless or even beneficial substances. Then the toxins that cannot remain in the body after a treatment do not have to be processed out; they are just transformed. This transformation usually does not cause any symptoms.

Strange Energy

By the term "strange energy," I mean simply any kind of energy that the body does not consider its own and wants to have released. I generally encounter three different kinds of strange energy in treatments. The first is an entity living in the client's energy field or in his body. The second is various types of energetic devices that block energy flow and energy connections and/or feed dysfunctional information into the system. The third is another person's emotional energy that has penetrated the shield of the energy body and gotten stuck in the system.

Entities

One type of entity that I have found is a human being who died and is therefore bodiless. It is my understanding that people who die are no longer meant to hang around planet Earth. They need to leave and go into the appropriate energetic plane. However, I have seen a great number of people who did not even know that they were dead. Imagine a person who lives a totally materialistic life in which nothing except physical matter is real. He might think that with death, everything is over. The possibility that consciousness might not be tied to a physical body is totally alien to him. When he dies, he finds that things are not all that different. He can still hear, see, talk, move and so on. He sees that he still has a body. However, he can no longer physically move anything and no one can hear him. He discovers that he cannot participate in life the way that he used to on planet Earth.

Some people like this feel frightened and totally lost. All they know is life on the physical plane and so they try desperately to participate in someone else's life. For this, they have at least to hang out in someone else's energy body, or even better in their physical body. This allows them to participate in and influence their host's thoughts, feelings and actions. Others try to find a house in which to live. That's why these entities inhabit houses that have been empty for a while.

Once you can see all this, you become aware of the most incredible and bizarre situations that you can imagine. This was just a little example to give you an idea of what's going on.

Other kinds of entities live in different frequencies on the energetic plane. Through certain affinities you have or things you do, you might attract them into your energy field or your physical body. I discuss this more in the section about drugs, on page 242. Entities also live in the energy field of the Earth in certain areas on the planet.

If you have an entity of some kind living in your energy body or even your physical body, this has a number of consequences. First, you think and feel everything that this entity thinks and feels to some degree. Some entities consciously know how to influence your thoughts and feelings, and they might try to make you do what they want.

Second, they often attach to particular places in the energy or physical body. This can block the energy exchanges among parts of the physical body, between the energy body and the physical body and within the energy body. This, in turn, can cause all kinds of diseases. They can also transfer information from their energy body into yours and so cause symptoms and/or damage the body.

The human energy body provides a perfect protection against any kind of entity that wants to hang onto it or enter the physical body. In its healthy state, it is like a shield of light that no energetic being can penetrate. This is something that I have both observed and read in books by people who are aware of these sorts of things.

Sometimes, an entity manages to penetrate this shield. The most common reason for this is an affinity of some sort. This can be an agreement, or simply a resonance that comes from similar emotional or mental patterns. The affinity allows the entity to either stay in your energy field or even penetrate it and enter your body.

Shield penetration can also happen when a person who died has a strong bond to someone still in a physical body, and one or both is not willing to let the other go. It can also happen if the energy body has openings that allow an entity to enter the physical body. This is quite common and happens mostly through drugs like marijuana. Energetic entities can also enter an energy field or physical body when someone loses consciousness through a surgical anesthetic or an accident, for example. A foreign entity in your body can lead to serious symptoms and troubles of all kinds.

My experience working in this area has taught me a few important things. For one, when you find an entity living in someone's body, nothing is wrong with this. It only happens through mutual agreement, of which people are usually not consciously aware. It is not up to the practitioner to judge whether such an agreement is good or bad. It is neither; it just is. Above all, the situation needs to be respected and honored.

For another, you need a way to protect yourself, and I have one important thing to share in this regard. When I first started this work, I sometimes had beings come into my field from another person. This was both annoying and frightening, because I did not quite know what to do about it. I tried all sorts of things, including rituals for protection and so on. They never worked as reliably as I wanted. Eventually I found out that being as neutral and non-judgmental as I could did the job to a certain degree, but I was still not totally happy with the results. Finally, I understood that love is the key. If you love whatever comes in your direction, you understand that it is a part of God. From what do you still need protection? Once you are loving, everything you attract will be loving as well. This means that every being that is exposed to love will either love back or leave. This changed my whole attitude about these entities. The more I stay in a loving space, the more I remain free from this kind of disturbance.

You need to do some other things to set the parameters of the energetic space in which you work when you practice RCT, but this is part of the practitioner training.

In an RCT treatment, the places in your client's energy body that have an affinity to an entity change frequency. When the affinity is gone, the entity literally pops out. In the second part of the treatment a higher aspect of your client often fills the empty space vacated by the being . These two things also prevent the entity from re-attaching.

Whenever you disconnect an entity from a person, you must also take care of the entity. Don't just disconnect it from another person's system. Make sure that it goes where it needs to be—which is not planet Earth. The angels provide a service on which you can call at any time. They will take care that the entity travels to the best possible destination for its evolution. However, you have to ask the angels every time, because their integrity is such that they only come to help when they are requested to do so.

Devices in the Energy Body

The second kind of strange energy consists of devices in the energy body. These devices are like programs that hold dysfunctional information and can cause a wide variety of symptoms.

In my experience, these devices are generally placed in the body in one of two ways. First, someone may have acquired them in a past life in times when humankind was much further evolved than it is right now. I do not measure evolution by the standards of technology, but rather by the development of skills and mental insights. In those times, many people had abilities that almost no one has today, such as telekinesis, teleportation and numerous kinds of manipulation of physical and energetic reality through the power of the mind. Having these abilities did not necessarily equate with high moral integrity or the capacity for love.

Many wars and much fighting also took place. Most people knew that death is no more than the disconnection of the energy body from the physical body and a transition into another dimension.. Therefore, shooting and killing did not make much sense to them. They knew that after a certain time, they could confront their enemy incarnated in a new body. Consequently, they fought largely by manipulating the energy body. This could produce damage that lasted longer than just one lifetime.

The second way to get an energetic device is to put it there yourself. By far, the most common reason to do this is as follows. Imagine yourself in unity, in all the glory of who you truly are. Then you decide to have a human experience. Coming here as essence will not provide that. Human experience starts when you connect to only a little bit of who you are, and you live blind to your own true being for a while. Within the course of your life, you can decide to remember more and more of who you are. This is one of the most beautiful experiences that you can have on this planet.

To experience this remembering or reconnecting, you must first forget your essence by seriously limiting yourself. Therefore, you set these devices in your energy body according to a meticulous plan, including how they must work and the parameters for their release.

If you were consciously aware of all this, you would not need the devices any more.

Some people also put limiting devices in their energy body due to feelings of guilt. They use a device to try to punish themselves for past life actions. Sometimes these devices carry specific information to prevent things from happening that caused a lot of damage in former lifetimes.

These devices can cause anything from minor symptoms to life threatening conditions. Many times longstanding symptoms disappear in an instant with the release of a device like this. They frequently lie dormant in the energy body and wake up when the frequency of the affected person goes beyond a certain threshold. Then they start causing more and more symptoms and trouble.

The treatment for these devices is the same as for the entities. By raising the frequency of the places where the devices connect, the affinity between the client and the device disappears and they simply leave the system. However, the client's own mind often creates these devices in the first place. Therefore, part of the healing of these structures involves healing the aspect of the mind that produced them. With this, the mind stops creating them and they simply dissolve. Usually the person`s higher aspects fill the empty places where the device existed.

I had a client who came in with pain in his big toe that he had had for years. He had tried a wide variety of treatments, but pain killers were the only thing that had given him relief.. It took only one treatment to get an energetic device out of his toe and the pain was gone.

Foreign Emotional Energy

The third type of strange energy looks to me like grey or black energy spirals that come out of some place in the body. These energies are usually acquired in childhood.

As we have already learned, the energy body shields us from energies that are not supposed to come into the energetic or physical body. This shielding function appears to be fully developed when a person reaches adulthood. Children do not seem to have an energy body that provides this type of clear boundary. If, for example, an adult is exposed to anger, it will most likely just bounce off his system. This is generally not the case with children. Many times the energy goes right through their energy bodies and into their physical bodies. If the child has a way to deal with this event, to understand that he is innocent and not responsible for the anger, he will most likely release the angry energy within a short time. If the child has nobody with whom to talk, no way to deal with the event and/or feels guilty, these energies will most likely get stuck in the child's system. They can stay there for the rest of his life.

Anger is not the only type of emotion that can cause this. Any emotion that is strong enough can penetrate the energy body of a child and get stuck in the physical body. This kind of strange energy also has the capacity to cause a wide variety of symptoms.

The treatment for this is the same as for all treatments for strange energy. The places where the strange energy connects change frequency and then it cannot stay any longer and pops out of the system. Often a treatment of the emotional and mental body follows in order to integrate the structures in the mind related to the original event.

Remember that in RCT, you cannot just charge ahead and release entities, devices and other strange energies. The client is only ready for this release when the body shows them for treatment.

Agreements, Vows and Contracts

Many people took vows or made agreements and contracts in former lifetimes. The situations that gave rise to the vows or contracts were often highly charged with energy. These contracts, vows or agreements then left strong imprints in the energy bodies of the people involved, imprints that can have a strong influence on them for many lives to come. Agreements, vows or contracts that have a limiting or damaging effect in later lifetimes were usually not motivated by love, but rather by greed, hunger for power or fear.

These agreements can be broken consciously if someone who knows how to do this is available. Usually this person has to be able to access the content of an agreement and then it is broken through the spoken word.

I learned the vow breaking procedure by observing lightbody surgeons and I have done it a number of times with good results. Subsequently, I found that it is almost always enough to connect the memory of the initial situation and/or the other imprints that it left in the energy body to a higher aspect of the client's self. With this connection to a higher frequency, they simply vanish out of the system because they were created at a significantly lower frequency. Finally, we are again looking at a person's reinterpretation of his past in his own mind through the connection to his higher aspects. With this, he sees the creation of the old agreements, vows and contracts differently in their entire context. As a result, his history will stop repeating itself. The process of conscious vow breaking is something very powerful and should be handled with great care.

Walk-Ins

A walk-in is a rather rare phenomenon. I will still speak about this, because a walk-in might come your way, and then it is very important to know what to do and especially what not to do. To deal with walk-ins, requires a high level of skill and experience on the part of a practitioner. A walk-in is the result of an agreement that is made prior to a person's coming into a physical body here on Earth.

We all set up our lifetimes here meticulously. Our plans usually include a variety of agreements with other people who will be here at the same time. Sometimes these agreements involve a highly unusual arrangement—donating our body to another consciousness at the time of our death. We call the body's recipient a "walk-in." I'll create a hypothetical scenario to illustrate this kind of contract.

Perhaps you are floating in the energetic realms, planning a lifetime on Earth. You look over your whole future life with all its possibilities, and you see that you will die by accident at age thirty-two. This event is set and inevitable. Before this accident, your body will be in good shape.

Other beings up there also have the ability to look into your upcoming life. One of them would love to come down to Earth to take care of some business, but he can't find parents with the right affinity.

He looks at your life and thinks: "This looks like a healthy body. The guy is well-educated, well-situated in life and so on. What a waste!"

He decides to approach you and asks you if he can have your body after you let it go. The two of you ask Spirit if it is okay and Spirit agrees. You then make a contract which states that the accident, though lethal, will not cause any major damage to your body, and that the other being will come into this body the moment that you leave.

You incarnate, enjoy your life and forget everything about this contract. The time for death comes and the accident occurs. The shock of this event facilitates you leaving your body and, in the same moment, the other soul comes in.

The first thing that happens in any accident is that shock causes the victim to leave the body as much as possible. In this case, we have a complete disconnection, which we call death. At the exact moment that you exit, the other being comes in. The body consciousness does not know anything about all this. It is busy dealing with the impact of the accident. Suddenly, another consciousness that is completely alien to the body is trying to enter. Most often, the body then more or less freaks out and is not willing to let this new consciousness come in. As a result, I have seen walk-ins who lived out of their bodies for years, unable to connect. On top of this, most walk-ins forget who they are over time. They literally drown in the memories stored in the body that they entered and identify themselves more and more with it.

This is usually what you find when a walk-in comes for treatment. The individual feels confused and disconnected from himself. He might know that something unusual is going on, but doesn't know what it is.

Since most walk-ins enter the body during a traumatic event, they tend to forget the circumstances of their entry pretty quickly. This trauma is usually a very strong one, because the disconnection of the predecessor is the same as death. However, the body did not die. Somebody else came in instead. This is something quite dramatic that the body has to figure out.

It seems to be important to the healing process that at some point walk-ins become aware of who they are and the nature of their relationship to their bodies. Some come in consciously, rather than during a traumatic event; they usually are and remain aware that they are walk-ins.

Because walk-ins enter bodies that have been built and imprinted by another consciousness, they enter into a system of agreements and relationships that are not theirs. In my experience, if they find themselves in an intimate relationship, they soon leave it. Some completely drop out of the circles of people related to their predecessor; some don't. This depends highly on the original agreement that states which relationships to keep and which to leave. Often sensitive friends or family members recognize a strong shift and that this no longer seems to be the same person.

On a structural level, walk-ins face the challenge of completely altering the imprint of the physical body that they have adopted until it is their own. This means that all the parts of the physical body that hold memories of the predecessor have to be changed. On a mental and emotional level, this can be quite a hard piece of work. They must constantly discern between what is theirs and what belongs to the body's previous owner.

I have worked with a number of walk-ins. RCT has proven to be extremely helpful both for connecting them with their bodies and changing the bodies' imprints.

If you ever treat a walk-in, it is critical that you understand that the body consciousness might have been tremendously traumatized by the change. If the soul who came into the body quickly forgets what happened and who he is, he has no way to deal with the trauma and help the body heal it. He identifies himself to such a degree with the memory that is stored in his predecessor's cells that he can't understand what is going on. It took me a long time and some experience to be able to tell whether someone is a walk- in. If you suspect that your client is a walk-in, don't talk about this until you are absolutely sure that it is the right thing to do and the right time to do it.

Drugs and Alcohol Use

I have made some interesting observations about the use of alcohol, marijuana and psychedelic drugs.

I see alcohol as a high-strung energy from the plant kingdom. If someone drinks too much alcohol regularly, his body can't absorb all the energy. The part that it is unable to absorb exudes back out, but at a much lower frequency than its original form.

A lot of energetic beings exist around us that can't live on as high a frequency as we can. The lower frequency of the excess alcohol energy is just the nutrition they like. If they find a source for it, they attach themselves to the drinker. The more that somebody drinks, the more of these beings he attracts.

They stay low key as long as they get what they want. If a drinker decides that he wants to stop, or even has thoughts in this direction, they become very active, because they don't want to lose their good source of food. Delirium tremens is the strongest manifestation of their efforts to get somebody to drink again. This happens regularly when someone who is severely alcoholic quits drinking. Faced with the loss of their supply, these beings raise hell within the person's energy system.

Beings who live at low frequencies are not the ones you want to be around. The highest frequency is the one of love. The lowest frequencies are the ones of hate, greed and so on. This gives you an idea of the quality of the beings that attach to an alcoholic.

I know of only one reason why an alcoholic stops drinking and this is because he wants to. Treatments with RCT will not make this decision for anybody, but they will create a free space in the mind that might make it a lot easier to make this decision and to stick to it. This usually happens for two reasons. First, many of these entities will be disconnected from the person's body, which will free him of their desire to have alcohol. Second, it is my experience that with RCT treatment many people are more in contact with the real needs of their body and mind.

I remember a client of mine, who came back after a week for his second treatment. I opened the door and before he even said hello, he started yelling at me:

"What the hell have you done to me?"

I said, "Er, nothing, what happened?"

He told me that he loved to smoke and after the treatment he had no desire for cigarettes whatsoever.

Marijuana exposes people to entities in another way. Marijuana is considered dangerous by those who make and enforce the laws, and harmless by those who take it. From my point of view, neither side really knows what it is all about.

As we discussed in the section on strange energy, many beings live on Earth without a physical body. They can be anything from people who died and continue to hang around to critters of every imaginable kind. As long as it is healthy, our energy body functions as an impenetrable shield against these beings. Pot, however, can create holes in the energy field when people smoke it. These holes grow increasingly pronounced the more pot is used. At some point, the energy field might look like Swiss cheese.

Many disembodied beings would like nothing more than to be able to participate in human life. Once someone opens up his field, one or several of these entities might seize the opportunity and jump into his body.

I have treated people who took a lot of marijuana and some of them looked like an astral zoo. When I looked into their eyes, so many beings looked back at me that I could not count them. Even if the user stops, without competent help, it can take a long time for the system to be clear again. In my experience, this is how pot affects most people who smoke it. However, I've seen a few exceptions; i.e., people whose fields remain intact.

Last, but not least, let's talk about the so-called hallucinogenic drugs, such as LSD, psilocybin, mescaline and so on.

Everyone's evolution unfolds in the way that is best for him. This means that the pace of evolution and the experiences that go along with it are designed so that people can handle them, proceeding neither too fast nor too slowly. Moving too slowly doesn't appear to matter that much. However, I have seen that moving too fast can cause serious trouble.

Once again, let's use an example. Imagine that all of a sudden someone's energetic perception wakes up and he constantly feels and thinks what everybody around him feels and thinks. On top of this, he constantly sees everything that is around him on the astral plane. Most people would either kill themselves or end up in a psychiatric clinic if this happened to them. I consider these expanded senses to be normal for every human being. Within the course of our evolution, when we are ready, they will wake up gradually and we will learn how to use them.

If someone takes hallucinogenic drugs, this can open up inner doors before he is ready. Some people can't close them again after this happens. They can then die or end up in a psychiatric institution. If they do remain stable, most of their energy goes towards keeping these doors as closed as possible and controlling whatever wants to come through. Without competent help, this can continue for the rest of their lives.

The people who remain stable, but must spend energy to keep the doors closed, are the ones that you will most commonly see in your practice. The experiences during their "trips" might have caused shock, even if they never reached the conscious mind. This locks down certain areas of the body and mind. Most of their energy goes towards keeping the emotional and mental system stable in order to maintain sanity and relate to physical reality in a reasonable way. This can stop their evolution, because no energy or space is left for this

This structure can cause any mental, emotional or physical symptom that you can imagine. People in this condition may not be consciously aware of what is going on in them. They might be completely clear in their everyday lives, but have a set of symptoms that they can't eliminate. Oftentimes, they are totally surprised when I explain the origin of their symptoms.

It takes a lot of experience to see when certain symptoms are related to the use of hallucinogenic drugs. Skillful treatments with RCT have closed these inner doors again successfully. The treatments help people get rid of their symptoms and return to a path of harmonic evolution.

I personally consider the use of hallucinogens to be extremely dangerous. Serious damage does not have to occur, but it can. The skillful use of similar substances in a ceremonial context is something quite different that I will not talk about here.

The Family Structure Connection

As practitioners of RCT, we can facilitate a very specific type of connection that can heal energetic imbalances that an individual takes on from his family of origin. Exposure to the work of Bert Hellinger helped me to interpret this type of connection. It actually seems to facilitate the same kind of connection and healing process that occurs in his family constellation work. I'll begin to explain it by drawing an analogy between the structure of a family system and the structure of the human body.

An Extended Understanding of Body Structure and Function

We can view a physical body as a unit that consists of individuals. Every integral part of the body, as we have learned, has a consciousness of itself; and with this, a certain amount of character and personality. In this sense, every organ, cell, atom, electron and so on is an individual. All these individuals serve a bigger purpose, which is to maintain the structure of a body.

As we learned in Chapter 7, if someone experienced an event he could not integrate, a lot of emotional energy that needs to go somewhere would float around his system. If the emotional energy stayed in his mind, his mind could become unstable. After a few of these events, the emotional energy could accumulate to the point where it resulted in insanity.

It is therefore of paramount importance that this energy gets out of his mind, so that he can go about his business and stay functional. Consequently, a part of the body volunteers to take on this emotion and insure that it stays out of the mind. This part of the body is innocent about the whole event. It is an act of love to take on the emotion and make sure that the system can continue to function properly.

Let's say that someone had an experience that was accompanied by a strong feeling of grief. This grief was so strong that he could not experience it and it had to be suppressed. Lungs are known to have an affinity to grief, and so the left lung volunteered and took it on. The energy of the grief takes up space in the lung and this has two major consequences. First, the tissues of the lung compress. Second, the process of taking up space disconnects parts of the information about structure and function of the lung. I described a similar process in Chapter 6, (page 63) and Chapter 7 (page 95) on the physical and emotional shock pattern.

You can read about the basic effects of lung compression in the section on lungs, beginning on page 207. They include misalignment of the biomechanics of the pelvis, neck pain, tennis elbow, carpal tunnel syndrome and so on. A certain susceptibility to infections, asthma and other trouble might also arise. Emotions that we can't integrate produce essentially the same consequences for the mind that I described in Chapter 7. They are a bit milder than those that accompany emotional shock, but are largely the same.

The mechanics for dealing with unintegated emotions in the body are analogous to those used by the family system for dealing with its energetic imbalances. Like the body, we can see a family as a unit that consists of individual members. If the family system has an energy imbalance, the energy has to go somewhere, otherwise the functionality, and with this, the survival of the family system is threatened.

The protective mechanism here seems to happen in the exact same way that it does in a human body. One member of the family steps forward and volunteers to take on this energy to keep the whole system stable and functional. The person who makes this decision almost always does so without being consciously aware of it. The person who takes on the energy of the imbalance has almost always nothing to do with the reason for the imbalance. To take on this energy is an act of love to ensure the survival of the family system.

As far as I know, the German psychotherapist Bert Hellinger was the first one to discover this dynamic. I am not sure whether he would completely agree with my way of describing it, however, this is how I see and understand it at this point. Most importantly, Hellinger not only discovered these dynamics, but also found a way to facilitate their healing. He uses groups in which the participants represent the family members of the person that seeks healing. If done skillfully, the results of this work are stunning and can be extremely effective. Without going into great detail, I will describe a few things to give you an idea of how the imbalances are generated, taken on and acted out in the person that takes on this energy.

Excluding one of its members is a common family phenomenon and happens for any number of reasons. With few exceptions, the exclusion of a family member causes an imbalance in the family system. Frequently, the person that takes on this exclusionary energy follows the exact same path as the person who is left out.

A wife who does not take her husband as her man, also causes energetic imbalance. The first-born son generally takes on this energy and balances it by taking his father's place. As a result, the son might not be able to honor his father as such, because he holds the father's position and competes with him. Later on in life, this can lead to the son's inability to maintain a relationship with a woman.

These imbalances can act themselves out over many generations. Bert Hellinger said that he had seen the dynamic of a hidden murder in a family continue to have an impact after fifteen generations!

These imbalances can cause any kind of physical, mental or emotional ailments. Please remember however, that RCT works beyond causality and the cause of an illness does not matter. As we discussed earlier, no such thing as **the** cause of a disease exists. Every cause has its cause, which has its cause and so on. For instance, I had a client who came because she had had headaches for decades. Her treatment was the family structure connection, and after treatment, her headaches disappeared for good. None of us knew exactly what happened in the family that created her imbalance or what she integrated. However, this information was clearly not necessary to facilitate healing.

With RCT, we can facilitate the healing of an imbalance within a family system, regardless of its nature or age. When a person comes for treatment and the body shows a need for this kind of connection, I can see that the treatment creates a shift in the family dynamics. All of a sudden, the client no longer has to carry the energy of the imbalance because it has ceased to exist. As I currently see it, a template for the whole family system exists on the energetic plane, and it reconnects to a higher frequency aspect of itself in the treatment. This seems to dissolve certain energies together with their effects. Moreover, the healing process bypasses the conscious mind in the same way that I described in Chapter 6, in the section entitled "Bypassing the Conscious Mind" on page 81. I have seen a number of phenomenal healings happen this way.

More than one of the frequencies I described in chapter 5 is involved in this type of connection. In fact it seems to combine several frequencies that belong to different centers. Some time ago, I had to give a specific initiation for this work to RCT practitioners who had been initiated previously, but it now happens by itself whenever somebody is ready for it. As I have observed, you have to be initiated into at least second frequency to be able to facilitate this type of connection.

Extended structures other than families such as tribal structures or whole countries also seem to operate in the way I just described,. These connections- for instance, the relationship of Jews and Germans, South Americans and Spaniards and so on- frequently surface in the work of family constellation therapists. They are potent examples of the perpetration of violence that still affect how people interact to this day and they show up to be healed.

RCT Birthing

My wife Kerstin developed the process of RCT Birthing. As we work in close proximity and share all of the birth processes, she asked me to share our experiences in this book.

In many treatments, I have seen trauma from the time in utero, as well as from birth, showing up for healing. This has happened with people of all ages, from the newly born to people of sixty years and more. To me, this means that a significant part of the population is carrying trauma from the time of their entry into the physical world. This trauma can strongly impact how a life unfolds, as it is among the first experiences in an incarnation. Realizing this, Kerstin and I started focusing on how to support future parents to facilitate birth without trauma. In addition, we investigated how to heal any trauma that does occur in the birth process as soon as possible. Imagine starting life without any trauma from the most significant experiences of all, your time in utero and birth!

Let us start with the process on the physical plane. Passing through the birth canal can put a lot of pressure on the child's body, especially the head and pelvis. I have found jammed cranial bones and sutures, as well as misaligned and jammed pelvic bones, from the birth process in people who were more than sixty years old. They had been carrying this all their lives. This can create a lot of tension for which the body has to compensate. This tension exists on the emotional as well as the physical plane, because compressed cranial sutures often create of a lot of emotional stress. What a way to start life if this is taken care of as it arises!

In January 2010, a friend of ours who is a midwife invited Kerstin and me to participate in a birth for the first time. Since we had to travel that day for many hours, we could not be as present in the process as we would have liked. The next morning we saw the newborn and I recognized immediately that her *os vomer* was jammed. The *os vomer* is the bone that sits between the hard palate and the sphenoid bone. I related this to the midwife, who in turn related it to the parents. The parents then asked me to treat their child, because she was not able to suck. I mobilized her *os vomer* and, almost instantly, the child started drinking at her mother's breast, which she was not able to do before.

The next aspect to consider is the emotional and mental one. It would be perfect if parents prepared themselves before they became pregnant, but to date, I have found this kind of consciousness to be rather rare. However, I think it is helpful to talk about this, even though we do not have much experience in the actual work, because all the parents who have contacted us so far were already pregnant. Although almost all the work we have done has come after the start of pregnancy, prospective parents can start the work before pregnancy begins. This will give them the advantage of doing the work for a longer time. In addition, if they take care of certain things, some of which we describe below, they will have a different experience of conception. I consciously include both parents in this statement because, in my experience, both the mother and father are pregnant. Though the father's experience is of course different from the mother's, he is as pregnant as she is.

Before we begin talking about how you can prepare yourselves for the arrival of your child, we need to talk about a highly important issue. Parents tend to feel deeply responsible for how their child turns out. They want him or her to be happy and successful. If this does not happen and the child grows up to be someone who does not match their definition of "happy" and "successful," they feel guilty. This tendency is extremely strong in almost all the parents I know. The feeling of guilt is about the most unproductive and destructive attitude parents can have in educating their children.

Please understand that your children do not come in with a clean slate. They have sometimes lived thousands of lifetimes and they bring imprints from these lifetimes which they want to heal. Almost every child brings something into this incarnation that he or she wants to resolve. In order for an issue to activate and rise to the surface, a similar experience must trigger it. Remember that we talked about this in Chapter 7. For example, if someone wants to heal misuse of sexual energy, he or she might be raped. If someone wants to heal something around the issue of violence, he or she might be born into a violent environment.

Before we incarnate, we have to find parents. To find the right parents, we must locate people who are willing to provide an environment that will give us what we need for our internal growth and healing. As we tend to forget this, step-by-step, once we are born, we do not appreciate some of the things that are "done to us" during childhood. Even more, we tend to blame the ones who agreed to provide these experiences for us, so we could grow and heal. A lot of people might refuse to be our parents if we come with a lot of stuff to heal. It looks to me like much of what happens during childhood is the result of pre-birth agreements and sets the stage for later. Once we become adults, we start our journey of internal growth. To be able to take full responsibility for ourselves, this knowledge is vital. Otherwise we might find it difficult not to blame others for what has "happened to us." Remember this when you feel guilty about your kids next time.

This might raise a question: Why should we do healing work with unborn or newly born children at all? Won't this take something away from the experiences they need in their lives?

We can always look at things from a higher perspective. Love can change things in an instant. Bring love into trauma and it dissolves. Love does not even see trauma, as it does not exist there. Remember that RCT is a way to apply pure love, and this is what we do. There is a way to lighten every child's load the moment he or she starts building a physical body, or, in other words, at conception.

I have been working with pregnant women ever since I started practicing RCT. When I treat a pregnant woman, the child usually receives a treatment as well. The treatment almost always heals past life experiences, unless another pressing issue is present. The children still have access to the bigger picture and their past life memories, and they love it when they receive this type healing. Their life can go on to a different trajectory, as so much of the baggage they brought with them is healed before they are even born.

Here we come back to how the parents can prepare for the conception and arrival of their child. Kerstin and I have encountered several areas that seem important:

1. Become pregnant consciously, meaning by choice and not by accident.

2. Heal and cleanse yourself as much as you possibly can on all levels—physically, emotionally and mentally.

3. Heal as much of your energetic family structure as possible. (See chapter on "The Family Structure Connection.")

4. Make sure that you and your unborn child are energetically synchronized at all times.

5. Take care to provide an energetic space into which your child can be born.

I will elaborate a little on these five points.

We have already learned that pregnancy is an agreement made with the parents prior to incarnating. Ask yourself how different an experience like this could be if you entered into it consciously, rather than just let it happen to you. One of the things we regularly have to impress on parents is that their lives will not be the same once they become pregnant, especially after the child is born. Many people seem to think that their life will stay the same, continuing as is, but with an additional person. Nothing could be further from the truth. Energetically, a family is a unit, consisting of individuals. (If you have not already done so, please read the chapter, "The Family Structure Connection," page 246). Marriage is more than a piece of paper two people sign and more than a prenuptial agreement—much, much more. When two people become legally married, their energetic system undergoes a significant shift; they create a new system that starts at that very moment. The arrival of a new soul into this system also produces a powerful shift, and the more people recognize this and its ramifications, the more consciously and responsibly they can be and deal with it. This requires awareness, and with awareness, parents can create an appropriate and supportive environment.

Remember that in a unit, the happiness of the other people involved is also yours and vice versa.

Most people seem to be unaware that children take on the unresolved emotional and mental issues of their parents. This is just how it is, and the process starts at conception. If you have an agreement to bring in a very pure soul, you need to clean yourselves up to the appropriate degree, otherwise this soul cannot incarnate with you as its parents. You can only attract a soul as your child where there is a resonance. You see, this goes both ways.

Children need a space into which they can be born. This is not only important on the physical plane, meaning shelter and a protected environment, but also on the energetic one. I have seen a number of families expecting a baby failing to provide an energetic space for this child. This phenomenon has a lot to do with the subconscious dynamics in the parents' minds, as well as with the dynamics within the family system. Children who are born into an environment like this can be quite unhappy and unsettled, as they do not know where they are and how they can fit. This can cause emotional unrest as well as physical disease. Experience has shown that the more conscious the parents are, the less likely this is going to happen.

To me, nothing in the world is more important than to care for our children. They are our future and the future of life on planet Earth. This care starts before conception and it starts with awareness.

This chapter is not meant to be a guidebook on how to conceive, give birth and educate a child; Kerstin and I might write one like that later. It is rather a description of the structures and dynamics we found around conception, birth and education. This chapter can help you become aware of these, and then, if it rings true, you can take steps. Awareness is always the beginning. I don't see how you can consciously implement change without first having the awareness that you want something different.

I am aware that you cannot do more than your best and nobody, maybe except yourself, is expecting this from you. So calm down, relax and enjoy the ride.

Besides all this, I assume that you want to know what we actually do to support a family during pregnancy and birth. When a woman or a couple comes to us and gets our "birthing package," we start working with them with RCT and address everything that comes up and can be addressed in this way. From the moment labor starts, we are available twenty-four hours a day to support the birth process. I do not like the word "labor" because it implies a difficult and painful process. Kerstin and I have found that birth can be completed within minutes sometimes, and be totally pain free and joyful. We therefore decided to call contractions "rushes," as in energy rushes, instead of "labor," an idea we found in a process called "hypno birthing," or the Mongan Method.

We have seen some absolutely beautiful things in our work. For example, children that did not turn were turned in utero, so they could have a natural birth. In other cases, the birth canal widened so the perineum did not tear. We always feel where the process is and we are there to assist it. So far, we have done all our birth support long distance. We work either with the midwife or another support person, who lets us know what is happening. After the child is born, we stay with the family as long as they wish. Here, we can help mobilize the biomechanics of the child's body that might have become jammed during birth, help heal emotional and past life issues and a lot more.

We can also help prepare the energetic environment into which the child will be born. We can support parents to learn about things that may be new to them, such as vaccinations and family structures. What we offer tends to be a mix of what I call "structural work," that does not require the client's conscious participation, and "conscious work," in which we might need the client's conscious participation, including expansion of awareness and particular actions, to achieve results.

Be aware that unborn children are aware of everything that the mother thinks and feels, and they can hear everything that she says and that others speak to her. Therefore, if you, for example, think about aborting a pregnancy and you end up not doing it, do not be surprised if your child has emotional problems even at birth. This actually goes beyond awareness. Fetuses feel and think everything that the mother feels and thinks and vice versa, as their energy body is within the mother's energy body. Your unborn child knows how to distinguish between a fleeting thought and a serious consideration. I did not choose this example for you to feel guilty, but to help you expand your awareness into areas that can be important for your child and you.

In the end, it is about love, which penetrates everything. All that is, is made out of love. You can allow yourself to become aware of this love that made you and that you are. You can allow this love to permeate every aspect of your life. Since most people are not used to this and go into survival mode instead, triggered by fear, it takes practice. One way you can start practicing is to bring yourself into the present moment any time you choose. It's easy. Just take one breath while fully conscious of what you are doing, meaning breathing. Feel this breath penetrating your body, every cell of your body. Then see if you feel any fear in this moment. In the present moment, no fear exists; fear belongs to the past. The present moment holds only life with its endless possibilities. Life will guide you from there if you choose to listen.

Our Love and Blessings to you and your children already born, in utero and yet to be conceived.

RCT for Animals

At this point I have treated all kinds of animals except insects. They all have the same basic energy-body structure as humans, and their energy body interfaces with the physical body in basically the same way. I have seen animals connecting up to the level of the seventh frequency of the first center and the fourth frequency of the second center. I have never seen the activation of the brainstem or the pineal gland happen in an animal. I want to share some of my experiences working with animals beginning with vaccinations.

Animals react to vaccines the same way as humans. Every animal vaccination that I have seen so far creates the same type of inflammation in the CNS and the gut brain. Vaccinations have the same limiting influence on animals that they do on humans. I already talked about vaccinations and their consequences. With reference to animals, I do have one more thing to discuss—the frequency of their vaccinations. For example, even from the perspective of western medicine, animals do not need rabies vaccinations every year, because the antibodies remain at a sufficient level in the blood for at least three-to-five years.

Animals have feelings and thoughts and they can be hurt. They put up mental and emotional protective mechanisms that are quite similar to those of humans. Treatments of the emotional body and the mental body can help to heal the mind of a troubled animal beautifully. I have seen this happen frequently, especially in dogs and horses. Animals seem to have multiple lifetimes and can come with a job to do and things they want to learn.

Like humans, animals are in different stages of personal evolution. Some are smart; some are not. Some are sensitive and aware; some are not.

Horses

I have been treating horses regularly for more than 10 years. The more I get to know them, the more they amaze me.

I experience horses as very sensitive animals. With most of them, I can have nonverbal, mind-to- mind communication that works just fine. Most horses sense what you feel when you are around them. Some, when they want to, can know exactly what you think at any time. For instance, once I was treating a big Clydesdale who had injured his front leg when his foot caught in a step and he stumbled. The actual injury was not a big problem to heal. Once I finished the last treatment, I wanted to walk away but it did not feel right. So I stayed and asked him telepathically what he wanted. Instantly he put his head down and pointed it a few times at his right knee. I took some more time to examine his right knee and sure enough, I found a microfracture in one of the bones from an old injury. I told him what I had found and that I would treat it when it came up, which would probably be in the next treatment. Then he let me go.

The mind of a horse, especially the emotional body, seems to connect intimately with its gut, as if the gut *is* the horse's emotions. Whatever goes on in a horse emotionally—and it looks as if everything in a horse is emotional—influences his gut. In cases of severe, acute stress, the mind can disconnect from the gut and the horse can die within a few minutes. I was once called by a horse owner whose horse started to experience colic after the death of his best friend, a goat. In the treatment, his emotional and mental body connected and the colic stopped instantly. The symptoms came back after awhile and required the same treatment. After that, they were gone for good.

More and more people are becoming aware of the true nature of horses and what they need. Animal communicators can play an important role in helping owners understand their horses. These people can communicate with horses and other animals the way that I can and they offer this as a service.

If you look at a horse's weight relative to the circumference of its legs, you can easily comprehend the delicacy of a horse's biomechanics.

Delicate, in this context, means that even a minor imbalance can produce suffering and lameness within a comparatively short time. Some people, for example, can run around with a dysfunctional sacroiliac joint for years, but in a horse, it can produce symptoms within weeks.

I find the same kinds of compressions and compensations in horses that I find in humans: compressions and injuries to the CNS, the circulatory system, the organs, everything I discussed previously. Compression, as you know, produces biomechanical misalignment. In horses, this creates the potential for becoming lame. Therefore, treating an inflamed joint, for example, does not make sense until you find what is pulling on the joint and heal this first. The same is valid for a chiropractic adjustment. Injecting a joint with an anti-inflammatory drug might help for a while. However, in the long run, if we do not elimintate the pull on the biomechanics that is causing the inflammation it creates a downward spiral in the horse's health.

Everything we talked about in the context of human biomechanics applies to horses as well. Many horses with trouble in their front legs have scars in their lungs from old injuries, abuse or pneumonia. These scars and shock patterns pull on the tissues of the front legs constantly and alter their biomechanics. Healing the lungs can align the biomechanics of the front legs and make the horse sound again, sometimes with just a few treatments. I have found scars and compression in the lungs to be the main cause of navicular bone disease. They produce a constant pull on the deep flexor tendons that go right over the navicular bone. This in turn causes compression in the navicular bone. This compression, together with reduced blood flow, can lead to the bone's deterioration. We have cured one horse with this condition that was considered unusable, mainly by restructuring and mobilizing the lungs.

A widespread problem in the U.S. race horse business is the so-called "wobbler syndrome." With this condition, the horse typically has difficulty coordinating certain movements, especially those that involve its hind end. This occurs in all degrees of severity, from barely visible, to the horse falling down and not being able to get up again under its own power.

This syndrome arises from spinal cord compression in the cervical spine. Its cause is a spinal channel that is too narrow due to incomplete development of the vertebrae of the cervical spine or injuries to the cervical spine. This can lead to cervical spine instability, which in turn can produce spinal cord compression. The narrow spinal channel can show up when a horse's natural growth process gets disturbed.

The race horse business seems to be mostly about money. You'll find few big auctions where one-year-old thoroughbreds are sold. Big horses generally sell for more money then small ones. Therefore, owners try to facilitate rapid growth. To do so, they sometimes wean foals at three months and then feed them with a diet rich in protein and carbohydrates, all of which is completely unsuitable for a horse's digestive system. One of the consequences can be inflammation and swelling of the spinal cord. The intention to have a fast-growing horse together with the measures just described can produce a disordered growth process (see "The Growth Process" on page 210). If the spinal cord grows faster than the spinal channel, this creates spinal cord compression.

We have taken on a few horses with wobbler syndrome, and we have been able to facilitate complete healing in some of them. Sometimes the symptoms were gone within a few weeks of starting treatments. For a few horses that we have treated over many months, the healing process is continuing. Their mobility has improved greatly, but they are not yet sound enough to ride safely. The first thing we do when they come to us is change their diet to just grass and hay. We give them very little alfalfa and nothing with sugar

I have seen numerous other conditions while treating horses and addressed many of them successfully with RCT. These include acute infections, anything from pneumonia to West Nile encephalitis. It works about the same as it does in humans, so I will not talk about it again. I have treated other conditions that occur specifically in horses, but I don't yet have enough experience to present them here.

It is best to take care of compressions and other conditions within a horse's body before they actually start to produce symptoms. It looks like RCT treatments can contribute to keeping a horse healthy and sound into old age.

Epilog

Where does disease originate? Unless we answer this question, we will not know the origin of healing. I wrote this book to help you get to the bottom of things. We have seen that disease cannot originate in the physical body, as it is ruled by the energy body and cannot create things by itself. Therefore, clearly, disease has its source in the energy body.

RCT started revealing itself to me around the middle of 1996. I had been an enthusiastic classical homeopath since 1989. Occasionally, I put my hands on people when I had the feeling that it would do some good. All of a sudden, dramatic things began to happen, far beyond anything I had ever seen. During this period, my life also underwent some major changes and I decided to go on an open sabbatical, not knowing when or if I would start practicing again. From time to time, I would put my hands on people, and the results grew so strong that after a two-year break from practicing healing arts I decided to return. I offered this new "modality" without knowing what I was doing or having a name for it.

A few things became clear to me within the first few months after returning to practice. I learned that the healing effect in the treatment session happened by itself; I could do nothing to make it happen. It seemed that the more I relaxed and allowed things to go their way, the faster and more easily the effect manifested. However, I seemed to need a certain kind of intention for the effect to take place. It took me two years to solve that mystery.

I always knew in my heart the existence of God. I also knew that everyone knows this the same way I do. I also knew that we cannot teach God's existence, but we can touch the place where this knowledge resides, and then people remember. God is eternal, beyond description, beyond words. God just is. Touching this place is like striking a bell. When it rings, you hear and then you know. I was always aware that disease originates from forgetting God, forgetting who we are. For me, these are the same. I was looking for a "therapy" that brings people to God, because only then will they find healing and what their soul is looking for.

Having experienced it myself, I thoroughly understood how a traumatized mind reacts due to the perceived need for self-protection. I longed for a way to facilitate healing for this that was so easy that all we had to do was ask for it. And there it was: healing emotional trauma through the subconscious mind. When this first came to me, I was the happiest person you can possibly imagine.

Healing at the root of creation through connecting to the God that we are. Oneness. Reminding each other of our true nature. What a gift! How easy and natural! All we have to "do" is allow it to happen. The clarity about how far the conscious mind can take us and when we have reached its limits, we go further by just allowing things to happen. Intention and oneness.

After training people for a while, I grasped that practicing RCT is not like employing a modality or working a job. We cannot split into two people, one therapist and one private person. To be serious about practicing RCT is to adopt its principles into our life. This is natural, as they are universal principles that become increasingly important as we wake up. We start walking a path. We become serious about life. This does not mean that we stop having fun and become a "serious" person. Quite the opposite. Becoming serious about life means changing our focus and priority. Do we spend our life with distractions or learning and applying the principles of creation? The more I comprehend the principles of creation and apply these to my life, the more joyful I become.

All we need to know, we already are. Therein lays the challenge: We have forgotten. Students asked me in classes, "What attitude is most helpful for our internal development?" I needed some time to sit with this. It is humility, and then nothing comes for a long time. Then, more humility, and again there is nothing for a long time…and then, even more humility. Humility is born out of the experience that before God we know nothing. Any thought we have, any concept, is nothing. What we truly are is so much more than the mind can conceive.

How do we remember God? What can we do? A dear friend, in her sometimes beautiful and drastic way, bottom-lined it: "Shut up!!" This was her way of saying that the mind cannot contribute to knowing God, only the heart can. The heart works in silence, beyond words and concepts. It is the gateway to the inner space where things are born anew, and where reality resides that is always new and flowing. The mind must bow to the heart, acknowledging its superiority. The mind has been on a rampage, creating the belief in separation. It cannot undo this without bowing to the heart, as only the heart truly knows God.

Healing in my understanding is reminding each other who we are in our essence. God is highly contagious. As you wake up to your true being, you become healing to others, and there is nothing you can do about it. Just your presence stimulates the memory of their true self in others. The ego will put up a fight, which is where work and discipline come in. Unless you are a saint (and maybe not even then), you cannot accomplish much in terms of awakening without discipline. You must learn to discern truth from falsehood. What is ego and what is love? What is from personality and what is from essence? Quiet time, meditation, being present, learning, paying attention: 24/7 is best. The rewards are enormous. Practice, practice, practice.

Learning about awareness and choice is powerful. Have awareness first, then make your choice, otherwise, you might make a poor one. Awareness grows from dedication to the path.

The universe busts its butt for those who are committed. They will have everything they need and lack nothing.

In my experience, the greatest gift to the life of those who are awakening is a living master. A master can accelerate us on our path to an inexpressible degree. He or she can serve as an open door to grace that flows for us unceasingly. The master is with us and uses any opening to work with us and grace us. What do we bring? The same humility and devotion we use when we work with ourselves and we can give what we received to other people. A master is always in oneness. No difference or gap exists between a master and us. They are us and we are them. Masters can also present formidable challenges, as they bring up all our issues. This is where awareness, humility and devotion are important, again.

We all use energy every moment of our lives. As long as we are not aware, we use energy subconsciously. We can be a myriad of different energies that are not aware of each other and the purpose they serve. They move in countless different directions at all times, without much of a common intention among them—or, at least among the majority— to move in the same direction. As we wake up, we become aware. These split aspects integrate, and more and more of them come under the rule of our higher aspects. Then we become a unified field of intention that sets energy in motion. We become purpose. We become a focused stream of energy that can accomplish things of which the sleeping mind cannot even dream.

Most people I know, consciously enter into the realm of energy because the ego thinks that there is something to gain. Money, power, glory, sex, all these things that are so very attractive to the ego. It does not matter. Eventually, we understand that death is the only thing available for this part of us. In the beginning and many times thereafter, we feel like we are dying many times over, as long as we believe that the ego is all we are.

We start having breakthroughs, moments of reality. They are so different from anything we have known, that in the beginning, they often fade from our conscious mind like dreams after we wake up. As our awareness increases, we do everything to keep them, but the memory is not the same as the actual experience. This can be disheartening, but it is natural, since so much identification is still with the ego. It is much like undergoing therapy. In therapy, we receive powerful healings, after which everything seems new and clear. However, soon the experience starts fading and we can't do anything about it. We begin to feel hopeless and that nothing ever changes.

I see these kinds of experiences as seeds. They are planted in the soil, and with this, they become invisible to us. It is not helpful to dig a seed up every day to make sure that it grows. Trust! Learn from nature; it teaches us all we need to know. The seed carries the imprint of the plant that it is going to become. We can give the seed love and a good environment in which to develop into a plant or tree, but it grows by itself and has all the information it needs to do so. We can do nothing to *make* it grow. How helpful it is to understand this! How similar this is to the principles of RCT!

Energy. We are energy. We are a living God. God created humanity in his image and this is what we are. The real desire behind all longings is to become that fully. Every one of us is unique. What we are cannot be taught; we can only remember it. Nobody can tell us who we are, yet we can remind each other of our true nature. All authentic teachings guide us to go within, as that is where we find the real treasure, and the treasure is our true self.

Being 100 percent true to yourself is mandatory on this path. Nothing is there except you.

May this book serve you on your path.

In Love,
Herwig

RCT Publishing

Langley, WA

To order additional copies of *Reconnective Therapy: A New Healing Paradigm* please contact us at:

www.reconnectivetherapy.com
orders@reconnectivetherapy.com
360-321-1207

Reconnective Therapy

Herwig Schoen and other RCT Practitioners treat people and animals and do regular treatment groups in the United States and Europe as well as long distance treatments on the phone. Training sessions are held in Langley, WA and other locations in the United States and Germany.

For treatment, class or training information and registration please contact us at:

Reconnective Therapy
5326 Mina Lane
Langley, WA 98260
360-321-1207
info@reconnectivetherapy.com
www.reconnectivetherapy.com